Solids and Liquids

FOSS

Next Generation

Full Option Science System™
Developed at the Lawrence Hall of Science, University of California, Berkeley
Published and Distributed by Delta Education

FOSS Lawrence Hall of Science Team
Larry Malone and Linda De Lucchi, FOSS Project Codirectors and Lead Developers
Kathy Long, FOSS Assessment Director; David Lippman, Program Manager; Carol Sevilla, Publications Design Coordinator; Susan Stanley, Illustrator; John Quick, Photographer
FOSS Curriculum Developers: Brian Campbell, Teri Lawson, Alan Gould, Susan Kaschner Jagoda, Ann Moriarty, Jessica Penchos, Kimi Hosoume, Virginia Reid, Joanna Snyder, Erica Beck Spencer, Joanna Totino, Diana Velez, Natalie Yakushiji
Susan Ketchner, Technology Project Manager
FOSS Technology Team: Dan Bluestein, Christopher Cianciarulo, Matthew Jacoby, Kate Jordan, Frank Kusiak, Nicole Medina, Jonathan Segal, Dave Stapley, Shan Tsai

Delta Education Team
Bonnie A. Piotrowski, Editorial Director, Elementary Science
Project Team: Mathew Bacon, Jennifer Apt, Sandra Burke, Tom Guetling, Joann Hoy, Jacquelyn Lachance

Thank you to all FOSS Grades K-6 Trial Teachers
Heather Ballard, Wilson Elementary, Coppell, TX; Mirith Ballestas De Barroso, Treasure Forest Elementary, Houston, TX; Terra L. Barton, Harry McKillop Elementary, Melissa, TX; Rhonda Bernard, Frances E. Norton Elementary, Allen, TX; Theresa Bissonnette, East Millbrook Magnet Middle School, Raleigh, NC; Peter Blackstone, Hall Elementary School, Portland, ME; Tiffani Brisco, Seven Hills Elementary, Newark, TX; Darrow Brown, Lake Myra Elementary School, Wendell, NC; Heather Callaghan, Olive Chapel Elementary, Apex, NC; Katie Cannon, Las Colinas Elementary, Irving, TX; Elaine M. Cansler, Brassfi eld Road Elementary School, Raleigh, NC; Kristy Cash, Wilson Elementary, Coppell, TX; Monica Coles, Swift Creek Elementary School, Raleigh, NC; Shirley Conner, Ocean Avenue Elementary School, Portland, ME; Sally Connolly, Cape Elizabeth Middle School, Cape Elizabeth, ME; Melissa Cook-Airhart, Harry McKillop Elementary, Melissa, TX; Melissa Costa, Olive Chapel Elementary, Apex, NC; Hillary P. Croissant, Harry McKillop Elementary, Melissa, TX; Rene Custeau, Hall Elementary School, Portland, ME; Nancy Davis, Martha and Josh Morriss Mathematics and Engineering Elementary School, Texarkana, TX; Nancy Deveneau, Wilson Elementary, Coppell, TX; Karen Diaz, Las Colinas Elementary, Irving, TX; Marlana Dumas, Las Colinas Elementary, Irving, TX; Mary Evans, R.E. Good Elementary School, Carrollton, TX; Jacquelyn Farley, Moss Haven Elementary, Dallas, TX; Corinna Ferrier, Oak Forest Elementary, Humble, TX; Allison Fike, Wilson Elementary, Coppell, TX; Barbara Fugitt, Martha and Josh Morriss Mathematics and Engineering Elementary School, Texarkana, TX; Colleen Garvey, Farmington Woods Elementary, Cary, NC; Judy Geller, Bentley Elementary School, Oakland, CA; Erin Gibson, Las Colinas Elementary, Irving, TX; Kelli Gobel, Melissa Ridge Intermediate School, Melissa, TX; Dollie Green, Melissa Ridge Intermediate School, Melissa, TX; Brenda Lee Harrigan, Bentley Elementary School, Oakland, CA; Cori Harris, Samuel Beck Elementary, Trophy Club, TX; Kim Hayes, Martha and Josh Morriss Mathematics and Engineering Elementary School, Texarkana, TX; Staci Lynn Hester, Lacy Elementary School, Raleigh, NC; Amanda Hill, Las Colinas Elementary, Irving, TX; Margaret Hillman, Ocean Avenue Elementary School, Portland, ME; Cindy Holder, Oak Forest Elementary, Humble, TX; Sarah Huber, Hodge Road Elementary, Knightdale, NC; Susan Jacobs, Granger Elementary, Keller, TX; Carol Kellum, Wallace Elementary, Dallas, TX; Jennifer A. Kelly, Hall Elementary School, Portland, ME; Brittani Kern, Fox Road Elementary, Raleigh, NC; Jodi Lay, Lufkin Road Middle School, Apex, NC; Melissa Lourenco, Lake Myra Elementary School, Wendell, NC; Ana Martinez, RISD Academy, Dallas, TX; Shaheen Mavani, Las Colinas Elementary, Irving, TX; Mary Linley McClendon, Math Science Technology Magnet School, Richardson, TX; Adam McKay, Davis Drive Elementary, Cary, NC; Leslie Meadows, Lake Myra Elementary School, Wendell, NC; Anne Mechler, J. Erik Jonsson Community School, Dallas, TX; Anne Miller, J. Erik Jonsson Community School, Dallas, TX; Shirley Diann Miller, The Rice School, Houston, TX; Keri Minier, Las Colinas Elementary, Irving, TX; Stephanie Renee Nance, T.H. Rogers Elementary, Houston, TX; Cynthia Nilsen, Peaks Island School, Peaks Island, ME; Elizabeth Noble, Las Colinas Elementary, Irving, TX; Courtney Noonan, Shadow Oaks Elementary School, Houston, TX; Sarah Peden, Aversboro Elementary School, Garner, NC; Carrie Prince, School at St. George Place, Houston, TX; Marlaina Pritchard, Melissa Ridge Intermediate School, Melissa, TX; Alice Pujol, J. Erik Jonsson Community School, Dallas, TX; Claire Ramsbotham, Cape Elizabeth Middle School, Cape Elizabeth, ME; Paul Rendon, Bentley Elementary, Oakland, CA; Janette Ridley, W.H. Wilson Elementary School, Coppell, TX; Kristina (Crickett) Roberts, W.H. Wilson Elementary School, Coppell, TX; Heather Rogers, Wendell Creative Arts & Science Magnet Elementary School, Wendell, NC; Alissa Royal, Melissa Ridge Intermediate School, Melissa, TX; Megan Runion, Olive Chapel Elementary, Apex, NC; Christy Scheef, J. Erik Jonsson Community School, Dallas, TX; Samrawit Shawl, T.H. Rogers School, Houston, TX; Nicole Spivey, Lake Myra Elementary School, Wendell, NC; Ashley Stephenson, J. Erik Jonsson Community School, Dallas, TX; Jolanta Stern, Browning Elementary School, Houston, TX; Gale Stimson, Bentley Elementary, Oakland, CA; Ted Stoeckley, Hall Middle School, Larkspur, CA; Cathryn Sutton, Wilson Elementary, Coppell, TX; Camille Swander, Ocean Avenue Elementary School, Portland, ME; Brandi Swann, Westlawn Elementary School, Texarkana, TX; Robin Taylor, Arapaho Classical Magnet, Richardson, TX; Michael C. Thomas, Forest Lane Academy, Dallas, TX; Jomarga Thompkins, Lockhart Elementary, Houston, TX; Mary Timar, Madera Elementary, Lake Forest, CA; Helena Tongkeamha, White Rock Elementary, Dallas, TX; Linda Trampe, J. Erik Jonsson Community School, Dallas, TX; Charity VanHorn, Fred A. Olds Elementary, Raleigh, NC; Kathleen VanKeuren, Lufkin Road Middle School, Apex, NC; Valerie Vassar, Hall Elementary School, Portland, ME; Megan Veron, Westwood Elementary School, Houston, TX; Mary Margaret Waters, Frances E. Norton Elementary, Allen, TX; Stephanie Robledo Watson, Ridgecrest Elementary School, Houston, TX; Lisa Webb, Madisonville Intermediate, Madisonville, TX; Matt Whaley, Cape Elizabeth Middle School, Cape Elizabeth, ME; Nancy White, Canyon Creek Elementary, Austin, TX; Barbara Yurick, Oak Forest Elementary, Humble, TX; Linda Zittel, Mira Vista Elementary, Richmond, CA

Photo Credits: © Alex James Bramwell/Shutterstock (cover); © Zach Smith; © Monkey Business Images/Shutterstock; © John Quick; © Christian Musat/Shutterstock

Published and Distributed by Delta Education, a member of the School Specialty Family
The FOSS program was developed in part with the support of the National Science Foundation grant nos. MDR-8751727 and MDR-9150097. However, any opinions, findings, conclusions, statements, and recommendations expressed herein are those of the authors and do not necessarily reflect the views of NSF. FOSSmap was developed in collaboration between the BEAR Center at UC Berkeley and FOSS at the Lawrence Hall of Science.

Solids and Liquids — Teacher Toolkit, 1487677
Teacher Resources, 1487611
978-1-62571-303-2
Printing 11 – 6/2022
Patterson Printing, Benton Harbor, MI

TABLE OF CONTENTS

This document, *Teacher Resources*, is one of three parts of the *FOSS Teacher Toolkit* for this module. The chapters in *Teacher Resources* are all available as PDFs on FOSSweb.

The other parts of the module *Teacher Toolkit* are the *Investigations Guide* and a copy of the *FOSS Science Resources* student book containing original readings for this module.

The spiral-bound *Investigations Guide* contains these chapters.

- Overview
- Framework and NGSS
- Materials
- Technology
- Investigations
- Assessment

The *Teacher Toolkit* is the most important part of the FOSS Program. It is here that all the wisdom and experience contributed by hundreds of educators has been assembled. Everything we know about the content of the module, how to teach the subject, and the resources that will assist the effort are presented here.

FOSS Program Goals

Contents

INTRODUCTION

The Full Option Science System™ has evolved from a philosophy of teaching and learning at the Lawrence Hall of Science that has guided the development of successful active-learning science curricula for more than 40 years. The FOSS Program bridges research and practice by providing tools and strategies to engage students and teachers in enduring experiences that lead to deeper understanding of the natural and designed worlds.

Science is a creative and analytic enterprise, made active by our human capacity to think. Scientific knowledge advances when scientists observe phenomena (objects and events), think about how they relate to what is known, test their ideas in logical ways, and generate explanations for the phenomena that integrate the new information into understanding of the natural world. Engineers apply that understanding to solve real–world problems. Thus, the scientific enterprise is both what we know (content knowledge), how we come to know it (practices), and how it all is interconnected (crosscutting concepts). Science is a discovery activity, a process for producing and applying new knowledge. The best way for students to appreciate the scientific enterprise, learn important science and engineering concepts, and develop the ability to think well is to actively participate in scientific practices through their own investigations and analyses. FOSS was created to engage students and teachers with meaningful experiences in the natural and designed worlds.

GOALS OF THE FOSS PROGRAM

FOSS has set out to achieve three important goals: scientific literacy, instructional efficiency, and systemic reform.

Scientific Literacy

FOSS provides all students with science experiences that are appropriate to students' cognitive development and prior experiences. It provides a foundation for more advanced understanding of core science ideas, which are organized in thoughtfully designed learning progressions and prepares students for life in an increasingly complex scientific and technological world.

The National Research Council (NRC) in *A Framework for K–12 Science Education* and the American Association for the Advancement of Science (AAAS) in *Benchmarks for Scientific Literacy,* have described the characteristics of scientific literacy:

- Familiarity with the natural world, its diversity, and its interdependence.

- Understanding the disciplinary core ideas and the crosscutting concepts of science, such as patterns; cause and effect; scale, proportion, and quantity; systems and system models; energy and matter—flows, cycles, and conservation; structure and function; and stability and change.

- Knowing that science and engineering, technology, and mathematics are interdependent human enterprises and, as such, have implied strengths and limitations.

- Ability to reason scientifically.

- Using scientific knowledge and science and engineering practices for personal and social purposes.

The FOSS Next Generation Program design is based on learning progressions that provide students with opportunities to investigate core ideas in science in increasingly complex ways over time. FOSS starts with the intuitive ideas that primary students bring with them and provides experiences that allow students to develop more sophisticated understanding as they grow through the grades. Cognitive research tells us that learning involves individuals in actively constructing schemata to organize new information and to relate and incorporate the new understanding into established knowledge. What sets experts apart from novices is that experts in a discipline have extensive knowledge that is effectively organized into structured schemata to promote thinking. Novices have disconnected ideas about a topic that are difficult to retrieve and use. Through internal processes to establish schemata and through social processes of interacting with peers and adults, students construct understanding of the natural world and their relationship to it. The goal for FOSS students is to know and use scientific explanations of the natural and designed worlds; to understand the nature and development of scientific knowledge and technological capabilities; and to participate productively in science and engineering practices.

Instructional Efficiency

FOSS provides all teachers with a complete, cohesive, flexible, easy-to-use science program that reflects current research on teaching and learning, including student discourse, argumentation, writing to learn, reflective thinking, and effective formative assessment practices. The FOSS Program uses tested instructional methodologies, including active learning, science practices, collaborative work groups, multisensory observations, integration of literacy, appropriate use of digital technologies, and connections to students' lives, including experiences outdoors.

FOSS is designed to make active learning in science engaging for teachers as well as for students. It includes these supports for teachers:

- Complete equipment kits with durable, well-designed materials for all students.

- Detailed *Investigations Guide* with science background for the teacher and focus questions to guide instruction and strategies for student sense-making of phenomena.

- Multiple opportunities for formative assessment at all grade levels.

- Benchmark assessments (grades 1–8) with online access for administering, coding, and analyzing assessments (grades 3–8).

- Strategies for use of science notebooks.

- *FOSS Science Resources,* a print and interactive digital book of module-specific student readings with strategies for science-centered language development.

- FOSSweb, a website with interactive multimedia activities for use in school or at home, streaming video, suggested interdisciplinary-extension activities, and extensive online support for teachers, including teacher prep videos, and instructional PowerPoints (for middle school) and interactive whiteboard files (for grades K–5).

- *Teacher Resources,* a collection of white papers and essays concerning instructional practice and techniques (Grade-level Planning Guides, Taking FOSS Outdoors, Access and Equity, Sense-Making Discussions for Three-Dimensional Learning, and more).

Systemic Reform

FOSS provides schools and school systems with a program that addresses the community science-achievement standards. The FOSS Program prepares students by helping them acquire the knowledge and thinking capacity appropriate for world citizenship.

The FOSS Program design makes it appropriate for educational reform efforts on all scales. It reflects the core ideas to be incorporated into the Next Generation Science Standards, and the foundational skills of literacy and mathematics. It meets with the approval of science and technology companies working in collaboration with school systems, and it has demonstrated its effectiveness with diverse student and teacher populations in major systemic reform efforts. The use of science notebooks and formative-assessment strategies in FOSS redefines the role of science in a school—the way that teachers engage in science teaching with one another as professionals and with students as learners, and the way that students engage in science learning with the teacher and with one another. FOSS takes students and teachers beyond the classroom walls to establish larger communities of learners.

BRIDGING RESEARCH INTO PRACTICE

The FOSS Program is built on the assumptions that understanding core scientific knowledge and how science functions is essential for citizenship, that all teachers can teach science, and that all students can learn science. The guiding principles of the FOSS design, described below, are derived from research and confirmed through FOSS developers' extensive experience with teachers and students in typical American classrooms.

Understanding of science develops over time. FOSS has elaborated learning progressions for core ideas in science for kindergarten through grade 8. Developing the learning progressions involves identifying successively more sophisticated ways of thinking about core ideas over multiple years. "If mastery of a disciplinary core idea in a science discipline is the ultimate educational destination, then well-designed learning progressions provide a map of the routes that can be taken to reach that destination" (National Research Council, *A Framework for K–12 Science Education*, 2012).

Focusing on a limited number of topics in science avoids shallow coverage and provides more time to explore core science ideas in depth. Research emphasizes that fewer topics experienced in greater depth produces much better learning than many topics briefly visited. FOSS affirms this research. FOSS modules provide long-term engagement with important science ideas. Furthermore, modules build upon one another within and across each strand, progressively moving students toward the grand ideas of science. The core ideas of science are difficult and complex, never learned in one lesson or in one class year.

FOSS Next Generation—K–8 Sequence

	PHYSICAL SCIENCE		EARTH SCIENCE		LIFE SCIENCE	
	MATTER	ENERGY AND CHANGE	ATMOSPHERE AND EARTH	ROCKS AND LANDFORMS	STRUCTURE/ FUNCTION	COMPLEX SYSTEMS
6–8	Waves; Gravity and Kinetic Energy / Chemical Interactions / Electromagnetic Force		Planetary Science / Earth History / Weather and Water		Heredity and Adaptation / Populations and Ecosystems / Diversity of Life; Human Systems Interactions	
5	Mixtures and Solutions		Earth and Sun		Living Systems	
4		Energy		Soils, Rocks, and Landforms	Environments	
3	Motion and Matter		Water and Climate		Structures of Life	
2	Solids and Liquids			Pebbles, Sand, and Silt	Insects and Plants	
1		Sound and Light	Air and Weather		Plants and Animals	
K	Materials and Motion		Trees and Weather		Animals Two by Two	

Science is more than a body of knowledge. How well you think is often more important than how much you know. In addition to the science content framework, every FOSS module provides opportunities for students to engage in and understand science practices, and many modules explore issues related to engineering practices and the use of natural resources. FOSS promotes these science and engineering practices described in *A Framework for K–12 Science Education* and the Next Generation Science Standards (NGSS).

- Asking questions (science) and defining problems (engineering)
- Developing and using models
- Planning and carrying out investigations
- Analyzing and interpreting data
- Using mathematics and computational thinking
- Constructing explanations (science) and designing solutions (engineering)
- Engaging in argument from evidence
- Obtaining, evaluating, and communicating information

Science is inherently interesting, and children are natural investigators. It is widely accepted that children learn science concepts best by doing science. Doing science means hands-on experiences with objects, organisms, and systems. Hands-on activities are motivating for students, and they stimulate inquiry and curiosity. For these reasons, FOSS is committed to providing the best possible materials and the most effective procedures for deeply engaging students with scientific concepts. FOSS students at all grade levels investigate, experiment, gather data, organize results, and draw conclusions based on their own actions. The information gathered in such activities enhances the development of science and engineering practices.

Education is an adventure in self-discovery. Science provides the opportunity to connect to students' interests and experiences. Prior experiences and individual learning styles are important considerations for developing understanding. Observing is often equated with seeing, but in the FOSS Program all senses are used to promote greater understanding. FOSS evolved from pioneering work done in the 1970s with students with disabilities. The legacy of that work is that FOSS investigations naturally use multisensory methods to accommodate students with physical and learning disabilities and also to maximize information gathering for all students. A number of tools, such as the FOSS syringe and balance, were originally designed to serve the needs of students with disabilities.

Formative assessment is a powerful tool to promote learning and can change the culture of the learning environment. Formative assessment in FOSS creates a community of reflective practice. Teachers and students make up the community and establish norms of mutual support, trust, respect, and collaboration. The goal of the community is that everyone will demonstrate progress and will learn and grow.

Science-centered language development promotes learning in all areas. Effective use of science notebooks can promote reflective thinking and contribute to life-long learning. Research has shown that when language-arts experiences are embedded within the context of learning science, students improve in their ability to use their language skills. Students are eager to read to find out information, and to share their experiences both verbally and in writing.

Experiences out of the classroom develop awareness of community. By extending classroom learning into the outdoors, FOSS brings the science concepts and principles to life. In the process of validating classroom learning among the schoolyard trees and shrubs, down in the weeds on the asphalt, and in the sky overhead, students will develop a relationship with nature. It is our relationship with natural systems that allows us to care deeply for these systems.

ACKNOWLEDGEMENT

FOSS is a research-based science curriculum for grades K–8 developed at the Lawrence Hall of Science, University of California, Berkeley. The FOSS Project is an ongoing research project dedicated to improving the learning and teaching of science. The FOSS Program is a curriculum designed to meet the challenge of providing meaningful science education for all students in diverse American classrooms and to prepare them for life in the mid-21st century. Development of the FOSS Program was, and continues to be, guided by advances in the understanding of how people think and learn.

With the initial support of the National Science Foundation and continued support from the University of California, Berkeley, and School Specialty, Inc., the FOSS Program has evolved into a curriculum for all students and their teachers, grades K–8. The Next Generation edition of FOSS is the result of a rich collaboration among the FOSS/Lawrence Hall of Science development project staff; the FOSS product development team at School Specialty; assessment specialists, educational researchers, and scientists; and dedicated professionals in the classroom and their students, administrators, and families.

We acknowledge the thousands of FOSS educators who have embraced the notion that science is an active process, and we thank them for their significant contributions to the development and implementation of the FOSS Program.

Science Notebooks
in Grades K-2

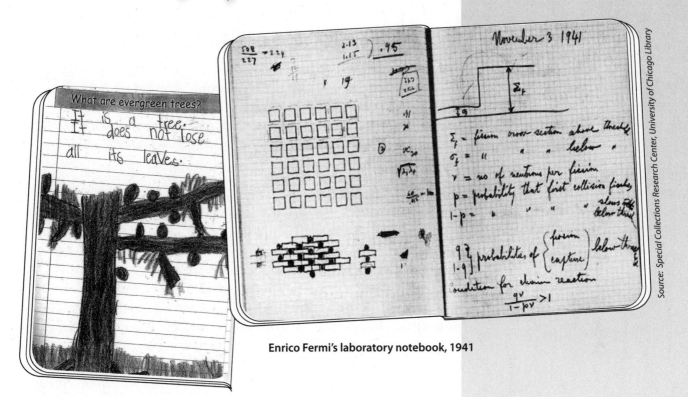

Student notebook from the Trees and Weather Module

Enrico Fermi's laboratory notebook, 1941

Source: Special Collections Research Center, University of Chicago Library

INTRODUCTION

A scientist's notebook is a detailed record of his or her engagement with scientific phenomena. It is a personal representation of experiences, observations, and thinking—an integral part of the process of doing scientific work. A scientist's notebook is a continuously updated history of the development of scientific knowledge and reasoning. FOSS students are young scientists; they incorporate notebooks into their science learning.

This chapter is designed to be a resource for teachers who are incorporating notebooks into their classroom practice. For teachers just beginning to use notebooks, the Getting Started section in this chapter suggests how to set up the notebooks, and the *Investigations Guide* cues you when to engage students with the notebooks during the investigation. For more information on specific types of notebook entries, the subsections in the Notebook Components sections include strategies to differentiate instruction for various ability levels.

Contents

NOTEBOOK BENEFITS

Engaging in active science is one part experience and two parts making sense of the experience. Science notebooks help students with the sense-making part. Science notebooks assist with documentation and cognitive engagement. For teachers, notebooks are tools for gaining insight into students' thinking. Notebooks inform and refine instructional practice.

Benefits to Students

Documentation. Science provides an authentic experience for students to develop their documentation skills. In the primary classroom, getting students to use a notebook will introduce the powerful skills of information organization. Students document their experiences, data, and thinking during each investigation. They create simple tables, graphs, charts, drawings, and labeled illustrations as standard means for representing and displaying data. At first, students will look at their science notebooks as little more than a random collection of words and pictures. Each notebook page represents an isolated activity. As students become more accomplished at keeping notebooks, their documentation will become better organized and efficient. In time and with some guidance, students will adopt a deeper understanding of their collections as integrated records of their learning.

Benefits to Students
- *Documentation*
- *Reference document*
- *Cognitive engagement*

Kindergarten entry from the
Animals Two by Two Module

Reference document. When data are displayed in functional ways, students can think about the data more effectively. Even with young students, a well-kept notebook is a useful reference document. When students have forgotten a fact about an insect or a plant that they learned earlier in their studies, they can look it up. Learning to trust a personal record of previous discoveries and knowledge structures is important.

A complete and accurate record allows students to reconstruct the sequence of learning events to "relive" the experience. Discussions about science among students; students and teachers; or students, teachers, and families have more meaning when they are supported by authentic documentation in students' notebooks.

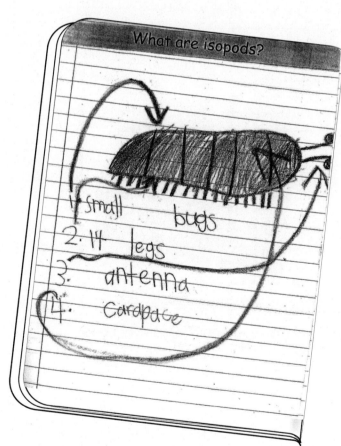

Labeled drawing from the Animals Two by Two Module

Cognitive engagement. Once data are recorded and organized in an efficient manner in science notebooks, students can think about the data to draw conclusions about the way the world works. Their data, based on their experiences and observations, are the raw materials that students use to forge concepts and relationships.

Responding to a focus question from the Animals Two by Two Module with a drawing and words

Benefits to Teachers

In FOSS, the unit of instruction is the module—a sequence of conceptually related learning experiences that leads to a set of learning outcomes. A science notebook helps you think about and communicate the conceptual structure of the module you are teaching.

Benefits to Teachers
- *Assessment*
- *Medium for feedback*
- *Focus for professional discussions*
- *Refinement of practice*

Assessment. From the assessment point of view, a science notebook is a collection of student-generated artifacts that exhibit learning. You can assess student skills, such as using drawings to record data, while students are working with materials. At other times, you collect the notebooks and review them in greater detail. The displays of data and analytical work, such as responses to focus questions, provide a measure of the quality and quantity of student learning. The notebook itself should not be graded. However, the notebook can be considered as one component of a student's overall performance in science.

Medium for feedback. The science notebook is an excellent medium for providing feedback to individual students regarding their work. Some students may be able to read a teacher comment written on a self-stick note, think about the issue, and respond. Other students may need oral feedback individually or in a small-group situation. This feedback might include additional modeling to help students make more accurate drawings, revisiting some important vocabulary, or introducing strategies to help students better communicate their thinking.

Focus for professional discussions. The science notebook acts as a focal point for discussion about students' learning at several levels. It can be reviewed and discussed during parent conferences. Science notebooks can be the focus of three-way discussions among students, teachers, and principals to ensure that all members of the school science community agree about what kinds of student work are valued and what level of performance to expect. Science notebooks shared among teachers in a study group or other professional-development environment can serve as a reflective tool that informs teachers of students' ability to demonstrate recording techniques, individual styles, various levels of good-quality work, and so on. Just as students can learn notebook strategies from one another, teachers can learn notebook skills from one another.

A teacher provides feedback to a student.

Refinement of practice. As teachers, we are constantly looking for ways to improve instructional practices to increase students' understanding. Your use of the notebook should change over time. In the beginning, the focus will be on the notebook itself—what it looks like, what goes in it. As you become more comfortable with the notebook, the attention shifts to what students are learning. When this happens, you begin to consider how much scaffolding to provide to different students, how to use evidence of learning to differentiate instruction, and how to modify instruction to refine students' understanding.

Kindergarten entry from the Animals Two by Two Module

GETTING STARTED

Starting in kindergarten, students are expected to make detailed, thoughtful records of their science inquiries. While this may seem like a lofty goal, with some patience and thoughtful support, both teachers and students can learn how to use science notebooks effectively.

A major goal for using notebooks is to establish habits that will enable students to collect data and make sense of them. Use of the notebook must be flexible enough to allow students room to grow and supportive enough for students to be successful from the start. The format should be simple and the information meaningful to students. The notebook includes student drawings, simple writing in the form of individual words and short phrases, and a variety of visual and tactile artifacts. When students thumb through their notebooks, they are reminded of the objects and organisms they observed and their interactions with them.

Notebook Format

In an autonomous approach, students create their entire science notebooks from blank pages in bound composition books. Students can glue or tape the provided notebook sheets into their notebooks, as well as create their own notebook entries. This level of notebook use will not be realized quickly and will require modeling by the teacher to provide enough structure to make the notebook useful. It will likely require systematic development by an entire teaching staff over several years.

You might choose to have a separate notebook for each module or one notebook for the entire year. (See the sidebar for the advantages of each.) Students will need about 30 pages (60 sides) for a typical module.

Advantages of One Notebook per Module:
- *Easy to replace if lost*
- *Lower cost*
- *Fewer pages*

Advantages of One Notebook per Year:
- *Easy to refer to prior activities*
- *Easy to see growth over time*

Organization of Notebooks

Two organizational components of the notebook should be planned right from the outset for primary students—page numbering and documentation. Two additional organizational components—a table of contents and an index—might be included only in the class notebook (detailed in the Supporting Students section) or in student notebooks toward the end of second grade. The teacher needs to monitor the time students are using for these organizational components. If science time is a premium, reduce the amount spent on creating a table of contents and indexing so students are able to fully engage in the four notebook components described later in this chapter. Not all organizational structures need to be present in individual student notebooks in the primary grades.

Page numbering. Each page should have a number. These can be applied to the pages, front to back, and referenced in the table of contents as the notebook progresses, or small blocks of pages can be prenumbered (pages 1–5 initially, pages 6–10 later, and so on) at appropriate times in the module.

A parent volunteer could number the pages. If students number them, monitor their work to make sure they don't skip pages or misnumber them.

Date, title, and other conditions. Each time students make a new entry, they should record certain information. At the very minimum, they should record the date and a title. More complete documentation might include the time; day of the week; team members; and if appropriate, weather conditions. When introducing a new condition to students, such as recording the names of team members, it is important to discuss why students are recording the information so that they understand the relevancy.

Some classes start each new entry at the top of the next available page. Others simply leave a modest space and enter the information right before the new entry.

Table of contents. If students keep a table of contents in their own notebooks, they should reserve the first two pages of the notebook for it. You will need to remind students to add to it systematically as you proceed through the module. The table of contents can be based on the names of the investigations in the module, the specific activities undertaken, the concepts learned, or some other schema that makes sense to everyone.

You might provide students with a preprinted table of contents without page numbers. As students work through each investigation, they record the relevant page numbers in their table of contents. If students are making their own table of contents, they should keep it fairly simple.

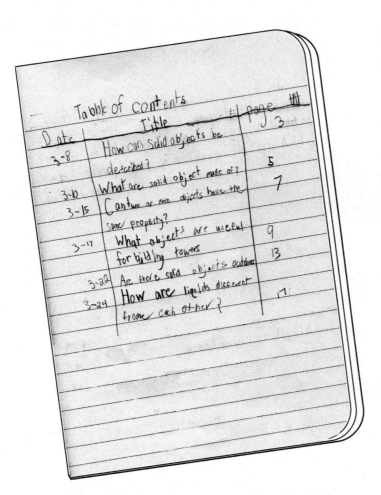

A table of contents for the Solids and Liquids Module

Index. Scientific academic language is important. FOSS strives to have students use precise, accurate vocabulary at all times in their writing and conversations. Key words can be displayed using a pocket chart, word wall, or written on index cards kept in boxes at each table. Another support to assist with acquisition of the scientific vocabulary is to introduce an index in the class notebook. It is not usually possible to enter the words in alphabetical order, since they will be acquired as the module advances. Instead, assign a block of letters to each of several index pages at the back of the class notebook (A–E, F–K, etc.); you or students can enter keys words. Students write the new vocabulary word or phrase in the appropriate square and tag it with the number of the page on which the word is defined in the notebook.

Including an index in the class notebook is a long-term time investment and can be overwhelming for the beginning notebook user. It may be better to forgo the index and use just a word wall to work with vocabulary initially.

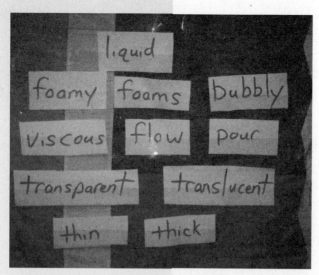

Pocket charts can be used to introduce vocabulary for students to include in their notebooks.

Notebook Entries

As students engage in scientific exploration, they will make entries in their notebooks. They might use a prepared notebook sheet or a more free-form entry. Students frequently respond to a focus question with a drawing or a simple written entry. Kindergartners may write single words; first and second graders will write simple observations and summary ideas, using the new vocabulary in their entries. These notebook entries allow early-childhood students to relive and describe their science experiences as they turn the pages in their notebooks.

Typically, the rules of grammar and spelling are relaxed when making notebook entries so as not to inhibit the flow of creative expression. Encourage students to use many means of recording and communicating besides writing, including charts, graphs, drawings, color codes, numbers, and images attached to the notebook pages. By exploring many options for making notebook entries, each student will find his or her most efficient, expressive way to capture and organize information for later retrieval.

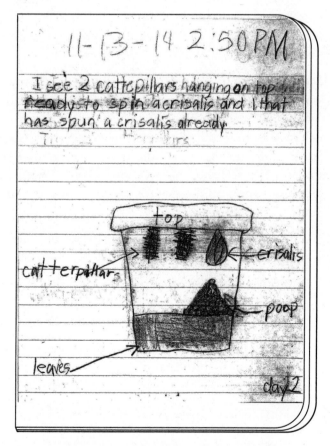

A notebook entry from the Insects and Plants Module

Supporting Students

Elementary classrooms contain students with a range of abilities, which is important to take into account when thinking about strategies for implementing science notebooks. Students need to have successful early experiences with notebooks. This requires planning. For younger students, a blank notebook may be intimidating, and they will look to you for guidance. FOSS teachers have had success using different supports and scaffolds to help transform the blank notebook into a valuable reference tool.

Class notebook. You can create a class notebook to document scientific explorations as a way to model the various notebook components. Use a chart-paper tablet so that the pages can be flipped back and forth, and make it accessible at all times as a student reference. The class notebook should be written in by both students and the teacher as display data. During the sense-making discussion, the class notebook should be visible. Students can contribute additional data, refine class-developed models, and build explanations directly in the class notebook. Students can emulate the class notebook in their own personal notebooks. Initially, individual notebooks will look quite similar to the class notebook. It is not the intent that students' notebooks be identical to the class notebook.

Scaffolds. Supports and scaffolds differ in one way. Supports are always available for students to access, such as allowing students access to a class notebook. Scaffolds are available just when the student needs them and will vary from student to student and from investigation to investigation. Scaffolds are meant to provide structure to a notebook entry and allow students to insert their observations into that structure. As the year progresses, the scaffolds change to allow for more student initiative. Scaffolds include

- **Sentence starters** or **drawing starters** provide a beginning point for a notebook entry.

- **Frames** provide more support but leave specific gaps for students to complete. Here's an example: "We planted _____ seeds and used _____ to water them."

- The suggested **notebook sheets** can guide students to record observations and data. The notebook sheets also guide thinking.

TEACHING NOTE

Use of the class notebook should be thoughtfully timed. Doing a class-notebook entry at the end of an activity is helpful to teach the components of a notebook, yet allows you to see what students do on their own. If you want to model a specific notebook strategy, use the class notebook during the activity.

Think-alouds. Think-alouds help explain the decision-making process practiced by a savvy notebook user. They verbalize the thoughts used to create a particular notebook entry. For example, if students have recorded observations about one type of rock and are going to observe a second type, you might say,

I am going to observe another kind of rock. I'm going to look back to see how I recorded rock information before. I see that I made a large, detailed drawing. I described the texture, size, and color of the rock, too. So now I think I will make a drawing of the new rock. I'm going to record the texture, size, and color, too.

Now I know that one way I can get ideas for what to write in my notebook is to look back at observations I wrote before.

Providing time to record. When young students are engaged in active science, their efforts are focused on the materials, not the notebook. Students need this time to explore, and many will not open their notebooks and record observations, even with prompting. Students need separate time to record observations that fully document their discoveries. Some teachers have found it easier to leave the materials on the table and have students bring their notebooks to a common writing area. Then the teacher revisits the focus question or task and provides a few minutes for students to record in their notebooks.

Dictation. Students could dictate specific information to an adult. The adult writes the information in the notebook for the student. Or the adult could write the sentence, using a highlighter, and students could trace the words, using a pencil.

Ownership

A student's science notebook can be personal or public. If the notebook is personal, the student decides how accessible his or her work is to other students. If ownership falls at the opposite extreme, everything is public, and anyone can look at the contents of anyone else's notebook at any time. In practice, most classroom cultures establish a middle ground in which a student's notebook is substantially personal, but the teacher claims free access to the student's work and can request that students share notebooks with one another and with the whole class from time to time.

Notebook Components
- *Planning the investigation*
- *Data acquisition and organization*
- *Making sense of data*
- *Next-step strategies*

NOTEBOOK COMPONENTS

A few components give the science notebook conceptual shape and direction. These components don't prescribe a step-by-step procedure for how to prepare the notebook, but they do provide some overall guidance.

The general arc of an investigation starts with a question or challenge, and then proceeds with an activity, data acquisition, sense making, and next steps. The science notebook should record important observations and thoughts along the way. It may be useful to keep these four components in mind as you systematically guide students through their notebook entries.

Planning the Investigation

Typically at the start of a new activity, the first notebook entry is a focus question, which students glue or transcribe into their notebooks. The focus question determines the kinds of data to be collected and the procedures that will yield those data. Depending on the timing and their previous experiences, students may be asked to record a prediction related to the focus question.

Focus question. Each part of each investigation starts with a focus question or challenge. The focus question establishes the direction and conceptual challenge for the activity. Write or project it on the board or on the chart for students to transcribe into their notebooks, or give them photocopied strips of the focus question to tape or glue into their notebooks. The focus-question strips are distributed as needed. Some teachers give students adhesive-backed labels with the focus questions printed on them.

Where does wood come from?

Notebook entry with focus question from the Materials and Motion Module.

> 3. **How can you sink wood?**
> Write the focus question on the chart, and have students read it together.
>
> ➤ *How can you sink wood?*

Plans and procedures. Students may plan their investigation. The planning may be detailed or informal, depending on the requirement of the investigation. These plans take time to develop and additional time to document in the notebook. A brief class discussion of the procedure may lead to a sentence or two recorded in the class notebook. This will be sufficient for many of the investigations.

Predictions. Depending on the content and the focus question, students may be able to make a prediction. When they make predictions, they are attempting to relate prior experiences to the question posed. Providing students with a frame can help them explain the rationale behind their predictions. A frame to help with stating a prediction is "I think that _____ because _____."

Data Acquisition and Organization

Data are the bits of information (observations) from which scientists construct ideas about the structure and behaviors of the natural world. Because observation is the starting point for answering the focus question, data records should be

- clearly related to the focus question;

- accurate and precise;

- organized for efficient reference.

Data handling can have two phases: data acquisition and data display. Data acquisition is making observations and recording data. The data record can be composed of words, phrases, numbers, and/or drawings. Data display is reorganizing the data in a logical way to facilitate thinking. The display can take the form of narratives, drawings, artifacts, tables, graphs, images, or other graphic organizers. Early in a student's experience with notebooks, the record may be disorganized and incomplete, and the display will need guidance. Students will need support to determine what form of recording to use in various situations and how best to display the data for analysis.

Narratives. The most intuitive approach to recording data for most students is narrative—using words, sentence fragments, and numbers in a more or less sequential manner. As students make a new observation, they record it right after the previous entry, followed by the next observation, and so on. Some observations, such as the changes observed in a mealworm, are appropriately recorded in narrative form.

Sentence frames provide a way for students to record their data. If students are nonwriters, they can dictate their observations, and you can write their observations in their notebooks, using a highlighter. Students can then trace the highlighted words.

A narrative observation from the Solids and Liquids Module

Drawings. When students observe organisms or systems, a labeled illustration is a very efficient way to record data. A picture is worth a thousand words, and a labeled picture is even more useful.

Some young students may initially prefer drawing their observations, while others may struggle to do so. When students make drawings, it can be helpful to suggest an acronym for making useful drawings. Accurate, big, colorful, and detailed (ABCD) drawings can capture structures of an organism, a balanced object, or an observation of a liquid. Think-alouds can also help students gain insight about not only what to draw but also when a drawing is useful.

It is not unusual for students to embellish their drawings by adding features such as smiles to flowers and living organisms. While this may be appropriate for creative expression, scientific illustrations should not be anthropomorphized. Give students feedback about making authentic observations.

Artifacts. Occasionally, the results of an investigation produce three-dimensional products that students can tape or glue directly into their science notebooks. Rubbings, disassembled fabrics, sand, minerals, seeds, and so on can become a permanent part of the record of learning.

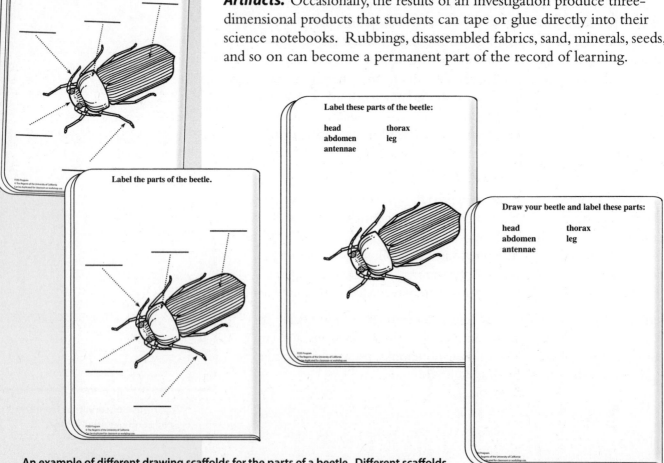

An example of different drawing scaffolds for the parts of a beetle. Different scaffolds can provide different levels of support for students. It is important to note that not all students need the same level of support.

Tables. When students make similar observations about a series of objects, such as properties of solid objects, a table with columns is an efficient recording method. The two-dimensional table makes it easy to compare the properties of all the objects under investigation.

Often, the preprinted notebook sheet provides a blank table. Students can quickly enter information on the notebook sheet. As students take on more independence in their notebooks, discussions about the column headings or the purpose of the tables shift the focus from filling in the table to the purpose the table serves.

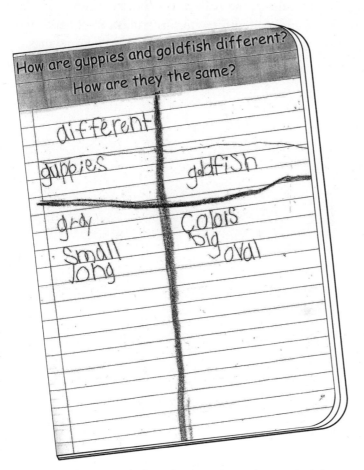

A simple table from the Animals Two by Two Module

Graphs and graphics. Reorganizing data into a logical, easy-to-use graphic is an important phase of data analysis. Bar graphs allow easy comparison. Additional graphic tools, such as concept maps and life cycles, help students make connections between data accrued during investigations.

For kindergarten students, you will need to model and scaffold graphs and graphics when students are ready. Visuals displayed in students' notebooks should also appear in a larger format on a whiteboard, projected display, or in the class notebook. You can use this larger display to connect organized data to the content students are learning.

Images. Digital photos of plants, rocks, and the results of investigations can be great additions to the science notebook. Finding a balance between photos and student drawings is crucial, as students need to develop those skills associated with making detailed drawings.

Making Sense of Data

The third component of documenting an investigation in the notebook involves analyzing the data to learn something about the natural world. Establishing the habit of thinking about the data collected and using them to help us answer a question is important.

Most of the sense making in the primary classroom takes place during whole-group discussions when students share, discuss, and analyze the observations made while investigating. This is called a sense-making discussion. During this discussion, questions are asked to help students interpret and analyze data in order to build conceptual understanding. Encourage students to use new vocabulary when they are sharing and making sense of their data. These words should be accessible to all students in the class notebook and displayed in the room. When students have limited written language skills, this oral discussion is important. This sharing is essential and is described in detail in the *Investigations Guide*. After sharing and analyzing observations, the class revisits the focus question. Students flip back in their notebooks and use their data to discuss their answers to the question. You scaffold the discussion, and use appropriate language-development strategies.

> **TEACHING NOTE**
>
> *See the Sense-Making Discussions for Three-Dimensional Learning chapter for more information on these discussions.*

---

8. **Ask questions to guide discussion**
   Ask questions to guide students' observations and discussion.

   ➤ *Were you able to sink the wood by attaching paper clips?*

   ➤ *How many paper clips did you use to sink the wood?*

   ➤ *Let's compare the two samples. Does it take the same number of paper clips to sink both kinds of wood?*

   ➤ *Does it make a difference where you put the paper clips on the wood? All on one side? Evenly distributed around all sides?*

After the sense-making discussion, students might review relevant vocabulary. Then they answer the focus question in their notebooks. In the beginning, you might model this writing in a class notebook, or students might work in small groups to write a collaborative response. Students could also make a drawing as a response to a focus question. As students become more proficient writers, they will begin to record their own written responses to the focus question.

A sense-making entry

Making sense of data is an opportunity for students to grapple with scientific concepts. The expectation is that all students will engage in this component. In many instances, using assistive structures, such as frames and prompts to guide the development of a coherent and complete response to the focus question, will help establish this expectation.

Thinking with evidence. In the primary classroom, students are expected to explain their thinking and provide some supporting evidence. While their explanations and evidence may be relatively simple, they will provide you with evidence of student understanding. A student might conclude that objects that have a round surface will roll because a ball and a can both rolled and they have round surfaces. The evidence should refer to specific observations, measurements, and so on.

For example, an investigation in the **Animals Two by Two Module** poses the focus question

➤ *What is the difference between red worms and night crawlers?*

Students observe and record, using the class notebook as a model. You create a Venn diagram, with input from students during discussion that compares the two types of worms. Students hear the focus question again, and they discuss their thinking in their groups. You write this frame in the class notebook

One difference between a red worm and a night crawler is _____ . I know this because _____ .

All students get a preprinted frame to glue into their notebooks and answer independently. Be careful not to display conclusions or other sense-making entries in a class notebook before students make their own entries. Otherwise, assessment of student thinking becomes difficult, as a student may copy the class-notebook response with little understanding of the meaning.

TEACHING NOTE

If students respond verbally, it is important to record those responses in the science notebook to establish that notebooks are a place to document understandings.

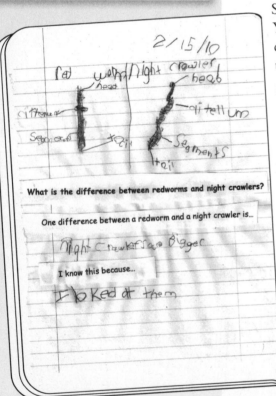

An answer to a focus question from the Animals Two by Two Module

Frames and prompts. Providing frames helps students organize their thinking. The frame provides a communication structure that allows students to focus on thinking about the science involved. This could be identifying the difference between two worms, students' thoughts about which types of objects roll, or how people can change the shape of wood. The frame does not do the thinking for students, but allows them to respond to the focus question in a clear, coherent manner.

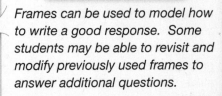

- *One difference between the red worm and the night crawler is _____ .*

- *I noticed that all the things that rolled _____ .*

- *I know this because _____ .*

I wonder. Does the investigation connect to a student's personal interests? Or does the outcome suggest a question or pique a student's curiosity? Providing time for students to write "I wonder" statements or questions supports the idea that the pursuit of scientific knowledge does not end with the day's investigation. The notebook is an excellent place to capture students' musings and for students to record thoughts that might otherwise be lost.

Wrap-up/warm-up. At the end of each investigation part or at the beginning of the next part, students will engage in a wrap-up or warm-up. This is another opportunity for students to revisit the content of the investigation. As they discuss their responses to the focus question with a partner, students may choose to edit their responses or add fresh information. This should be encouraged.

---

13. Share notebook entries

Conclude Part 4 or start Part 5 by having students share notebook entries. Ask students to open their science notebooks to the most recent entry. Read the focus question together as a class.

➤ *How can you sink wood?*

Ask students to pair up with a partner to

- share their answers to the focus question;

- explain their drawings.

Science Notebooks in Grades K–2

TEACHING NOTE

Students' learning can be assessed only at the level in which it was done. If students worked in groups to answer the focus question, it is difficult to assess individual understanding. Similarly, providing a frame to guide a student response provides evidence on what students can do at a supported level, not at an independent level.

TEACHING NOTE

These next-step strategies should be kept simple for primary students. The key idea is that students can revise their responses after gaining more information.

Next-Step Strategies

In each investigation, the *Investigations Guide* indicates an assessment opportunity and what to look for when examining students' work. The purpose of looking at students' work at this juncture is for formative, or embedded, assessment, *not* for grading. Look for patterns in students' understanding by collecting and sorting the notebooks. If the patterns indicate that students need additional help with communication or with content, you might want to select a next-step strategy before going on to the next part. This process of looking at students' work is described in more detail in the Assessment chapter.

A next-step strategy is an instructional tool designed to help students clarify their thinking and usually takes place before the start of the next investigation part. A strategy is selected based on students' needs. It may be that a student needs to communicate his or her thinking more efficiently or accurately or to use scientific vocabulary. A student may need to think about the concept in a different way. Because many young students are not able to articulate their thinking well in writing, it can be difficult to discern the area of need.

What follows is a collection of next-step strategies that teachers have used successfully with groups of students to address areas of need. These strategies are flexible enough to use in different groupings and can be modified to meet your students' needs.

Teacher feedback. Students' writing often exposes weaknesses in students' understanding—or so it appears. It is important to check whether the flaw results from poor understanding of the science or from imprecise communication. When students are able to read your comments, you can use self-stick notes to provide constructive feedback or dig deeper into students' thinking. The note might pose a question designed to move a student's thinking forward or to clarify an explanation. The student acts independently on the question.

When students have not developed the reading skills necessary to act independently on written feedback, read the question or prompt to the student. Language skills are supported when students have the opportunity to connect the written feedback to what you read to them.

The most effective forms of feedback relate to the content of the work. Here are a couple of examples.

- *Label your drawing to show the parts of the plant.*

- *Tell me why you think you were able to roll the ball into the "pond."*

Nonspecific feedback (such as stars, smiley faces, and "good job!") and ambiguous critiques, (such as "try again," "put more thought into this," and "not enough,") are less effective. Feedback that guides students to think about the content of their work and gives suggestions for how to improve are productive instructional strategies. Here are some examples of useful generic feedback.

- *Use the science words in your answer.*

- *Can you tell me why you think that?*

- *Why do you think that happened?*

Students return to their notebooks and read or listen to the feedback at the start of the next investigation. They can discuss this feedback with a partner during the warm-up time and refine their responses. You could model this refinement as a think-aloud or by using the class notebook. Monitor students to ensure that they are acting on the feedback provided.

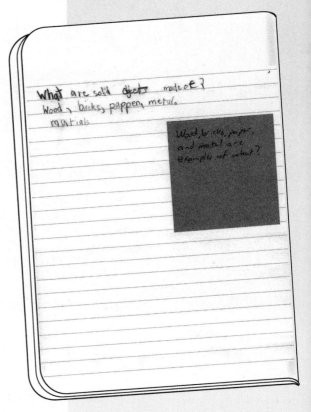

Students can respond to feedback by using a different color to show their new understanding.

Review and critique anonymous student work. Presenting work from other students can be a valuable learning tool for refining and improving the content and literacy of responses. Depending upon the culture of the class, you might present actual or simulated student work from a focus question or responses that reflect a common misconception, error, or exemplary work. Present it to the class in a common gathering area, such as on a rug, or display it electronically while students are at their seats. Present one simple response, such as a labeled drawing. Students then work in a group to discuss the merits and recommend improvements to the student response. In this process, students discuss what information is needed for a quality response. After critiquing other students' responses, students look at their own responses and refine their thinking. Students could also use a different-color crayon or pencil to make changes to their own responses.

Key points. Pose the focus question to the class, and, through discussion, elicit the key ideas or points that would completely answer the question. List only key words or brief phrases on the board. If you have already recorded the key points in the class notebook, revisit that list as well. Once the class has agreed on the key points, students review their own responses, looking for the key points. You can guide this by calling out each key point on the list, and asking students to put a finger on it in their notebooks. If students need to add the key point, they can add it in another color.

Mini-lessons. Sometimes the data from sorting notebook entries reveal that students need some information repeated or specific guidance on a skill. A mini-lesson is a brief interaction with a group of students that addresses a specific area of need. You might have a group of students observe a mealworm more closely in order to count the number of segments, or give students a writing prompt and work with them to explain their thinking more clearly.

> **TEACHING NOTE**
>
> *Engaging in argument from evidence is a critical practice that services a role in both sense-making and next-step strategies. See the Science and Engineering Practices chapter for more information.*

WRITING OUTDOORS

Every time you go outdoors with students, you will have a slightly different experience. Naturally, the activity or task will be different, but other variables may change as well. The temperature, cloud cover, precipitation, moisture on the ground; other activities unexpectedly happening outside; students' comfort levels related to learning outdoors; and time of the school year are all aspects that could affect the activity and will certainly determine how you incorporate the use of notebooks. The following techniques are tried-and-true ways to help students learn how to write outdoors and to give them all the supplies they need to support their writing.

Create "Desks"

Students need a firm writing surface. Students who write in composition notebooks with firm covers can simply fold them open to the pages they are writing on, rest them in the crook of their nonwriting arms, and hold them steady with their nonwriting hands—they can stand, sit, kneel, or lean against a wall to write. At the beginning of the school year, take a minute to model how to do this.

Many students feel most comfortable sitting down to write. Curbs, steps, wooden stumps or logs, rocks, and grass are places to sit while writing. Select a writing location that suits your students' comfort levels. Some students will not be comfortable sitting on the grass or ground at first. They will need to sit on something such as a curb, boulder, or wooden stump at the start of the year, but will eventually feel more comfortable with all aspects of the outdoor setting as the year moves along.

If students are using individual notebook sheets or notebooks with flimsy covers, you will likely want to buy or make clipboards. If you do not have clipboards, use a box cutter to cut cardboard to the proper size. Clamp a binder clip at the top to make a lightweight yet sturdy clipboard. If it gets ruined, no tears will be shed. If you're in the market for new clipboards, get the kind that are stackable and do not have a bulky clip. Ideally, all the clipboards will fit in one bag for portability and easy distribution.

If using a notebook sheet, simply put the sheet on the clipboard before going outdoors, and have students glue the sheet into their notebooks when you are back in the classroom. An elastic band around the bottom of the clipboard, or around a stiffer composition notebook, will help keep the paper from flapping around and becoming too weathered.

Bring Writing Tools Outdoors

Almost always, students will set up their notebooks indoors so that they know what is expected of them outdoors. If students will be recording data, they will carry their pencils and notebooks or clipboards outdoors and hold on to them the entire time. Make sure students understand how and what to record.

You can bring chart paper outdoors. Roll up a blank piece of chart paper, grab some blue painter's tape, and stick the piece of paper to the school wall. You'll need to tape all four corners. Or set up a chart inside and clip it to a chain-link fence with binder clips or clothespins when you go outdoors.

Take along extra pencils, as many pencil points will break. Some teachers find it helpful to tie pencils onto clipboards. Pencils should be tucked between the clip and the notebook sheet so that students don't poke themselves or, more likely, accidentally break the pencil points.

Another option is to prepare a cloth bag containing small pencil sharpeners, extra pencils, and other science tools, such as vials, hand lenses, and rulers.

Decide When to Write Outdoors

In general, notebook entries will be more detailed and more insightful if students can stay outdoors where the scientific exploration occurred. Sometimes, you will want to complete notebook entries indoors. If you are teaching the module early in the year when students are building up the routines for using the schoolyard, or if the weather is not ideal (a little chilly, raining, too hot, too windy), then you may want students to make notebook entries after returning to the classroom. If students are totally focused and in the moment, they can stay outdoors while they answer the focus question. If other students are outdoors playing, you may need to bring the class indoors to complete the written work. Only you will be able to determine what is best at the time.

CLOSING THOUGHTS

Engaging primary students in active science with notebooks provides a rich experience. Doing this successfully requires thoughtful interactions among students, materials, and natural phenomena. Initially, adding notebooks to your science teaching will require you to focus students' attention on how to set up the notebook, what types of entries students should make, and when students should be using their notebooks. You will establish conventions about where to record the date and title, where to keep notebooks, how to glue notebook sheets into notebooks, and when to record observations and thinking.

Once you are past these perfunctory issues, you can shift your focus to the amount of scaffolding to provide to students or to encouraging students to create their own notebook entries. During this time, you and your students are developing skills to improve the quality of notebook entries. These skills may include asking better questions to focus students' attention on a specific part of an organism or using color to enhance a drawing. Students begin to make entries with less prompting. They give more thought to supporting their responses to the focus question. When asked to make a derivative product, students thumb through their notebooks to find the needed information. The notebook becomes a tool for students to help recall their learning.

As students begin to document their thinking about focus questions and other queries, you may begin to wonder, "Should I be doing something with their notebooks?" This is when your focus shifts from the notebook as just something students use during science learning to the notebook as an assessment tool. Once everyone is comfortable recording the focus question and collecting data, you can take the next step of collecting notebooks and reading students' responses as a measure of not just how individual students are learning, but what the pervasive needs of students are. You choose next-step strategies that address students' needs before proceeding to the next investigation. The notebooks act as an assessment tool that lets you modify your science instruction.

This process will take time, discussions with colleagues, revisiting different sections of this chapter, and critical scrutiny of students' work before both you and your students are using notebooks to their full potential.

▶ **NOTE**
For more on derivative products, see the Science-Centered Language Development chapter.

Science-Centered Language Development in Grades K-2

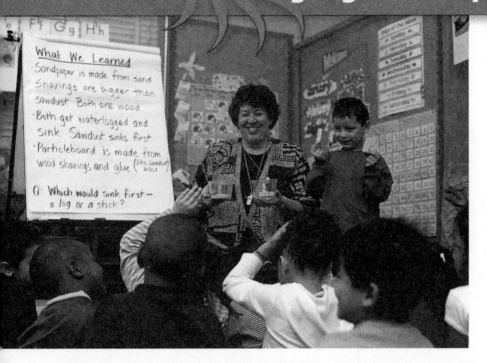

Contents

Teams of science inquirers talk about and write about their questions, their tentative explanations, their relationships between evidence and explanations, and their reasons and judgments about public presentations and scientific arguments in behalf of their work. It is in the context of this kind of scientific activity that students' literacy of the spoken and written word develops along with the literacy of the phenomenon.

Hubert M. Dyasi, "Visions of Inquiry: Science"

INTRODUCTION

In this chapter, we explore the intersection of science and language and the implications for effective science teaching and language development. We identify best practices in language arts instruction that support science learning and examine how student engagement in the science and engineering practices (SEPs) supports literacy. The active investigations, science notebooks, *FOSS Science Resources* readings, and formative assessment activities in FOSS provide rich contexts in which students develop and exercise thinking processes and communication skills. Together, these elements comprise effective instruction in both science and language arts—students experience the natural world around them in real and authentic ways and use language to inquire, process information, and communicate their thinking about scientific phenomena. We refer to the development of language within the context of science as science-centered language development.

Language plays two crucial roles in science learning: (1) it facilitates the communication of conceptual and procedural knowledge, questions, and propositions (external, public), and (2) it mediates thinking, a process necessary for understanding (internal, private). These are also the ways scientists use language: to communicate with one another about their inquiries, procedures, and understandings; to transform their observations into ideas; and to create meaning and new ideas from their work and the work of others. For students, language development is intimately involved in their learning about the natural world. Science provides a real and engaging context for developing literacy; language arts skills and strategies support conceptual development and engagement in the SEPs. For example, the skills and strategies used for reading comprehension, writing expository text, and oral discourse are applied when students are recording their observations, making sense of phenomena, and communicating their ideas. Students' use of language improves when they discuss, write, and read about the concepts explored in each investigation.

We begin our exploration of science and language by focusing on language functions and how specific language functions are used in science to facilitate information acquisition and processing (thinking). Then we describe ways to integrate English Language Arts (ELA) approaches and English Language Development (ELD) strategies purposefully into the FOSS investigations to both enhance students' learning in science and develop proficiency in the ELA strands of speaking and listening, writing, and reading.

Each section addresses

- how knowledge and skills in that strand are developed and exercised in FOSS investigations;

- literacy strategies that are integrated purposefully into the FOSS investigations;

- suggestions for additional literacy strategies that both enhance student learning in science and develop or exercise academic language skills critical for all content areas.

Following the discussions of the three ELA strands is a section specifically devoted to science-vocabulary development, with scaffolding strategies for supporting all learners. The last section covers language-development strategies for English learners and for students who need additional literacy support. The focus of this section is ensuring access to the learning experience as well as developing academic English and the language structures specific to the discipline of science and engineering.

▶ **NOTE**
The term *English learners* (ELs) refers to students who are acquiring English in addition to their native language(s). ELs are learning content and literacy skills in English simultaneously.

THE ROLE OF LANGUAGE IN SCIENCE AND ENGINEERING PRACTICES

Language functions are the purpose for which speech or writing is used and involve both vocabulary and grammatical structure. Understanding and using language functions appropriately is important in effective communication. Students use numerous language functions in all disciplines to mediate communication and facilitate thinking (e.g., they plan, compare, discuss, apply, design, draw, and provide evidence).

In science, language functions facilitate engagement in the science and engineering practices. For example, when students are *collecting data*, they are using language functions to identify, label, enumerate, compare, estimate, and measure. When students are *constructing explanations*, they are using language functions to analyze, communicate, discuss, evaluate, and justify.

The Framework for Science Education (National Research Council, 2010) affirms that "students cannot comprehend scientific practices, nor fully appreciate the nature of scientific knowledge itself, without directly experiencing the practices for themselves." Each of these practices requires the use of multiple language functions. Often, these language functions are part of an internal dialogue weighing the merits of various explanations—what we call thinking. The more language functions with which we are facile, the more effective and creative our thinking can be. Though students in K–2 are just beginning their formal explorations into science and engineering, they come to school full of curiosity and enthusiasm, ready to engage in the science and engineering practices at their level of development.

The science and engineering practices are summarized below, along with a sample of the language functions that are exercised when students are effectively engaged in that practice. (Practices are bold; language functions are italic.)

1. Asking questions and defining problems

- *Ask* questions based on observations about objects, organisms, phenomena, and events in the natural and human-made world.
- *Identify* questions that can be answered by investigations.
- *Define* a simple problem that can be solved.

2. Developing and using models

- *Develop* and *use* models to *represent* amounts, relationships, relative scales, and patterns.
- *Develop* models based on evidence to represent an object or tool.
- *Distinguish* between models and actual phenomena.
- *Compare* models to *identify* common features and differences.

Examples of Language Functions
Analyze
Apply
Ask questions
Clarify
Classify
Communicate
Compare
Conclude
Construct
Critique
Describe
Design
Develop
Discuss
Distinguish
Draw
Enumerate
Estimate
Evaluate
Experiment
Explain
Formulate
Generalize
Group
Identify
Infer
Interpret
Justify
Label
List
Make a claim
Measure
Model
Observe
Organize
Plan
Predict
Provide evidence
Reason
Record
Represent
Revise
Sequence
Solve
Sort
Strategize
Summarize

3. Planning and carrying out investigations

- With guidance, *plan* and conduct investigations with peers (K).

- *Plan* and conduct investigations collaboratively to *produce* data as evidence to *answer* a question.

- *Evaluate* different ways of observing and *measuring* a phenomenon to *determine* how to *answer* a question.

- Observe, *measure,* and collect data to make *comparisons* and to *determine* if a proposed object, tool, or solution solves a problem or meets a goal.

- *Predict* outcomes based on prior experience.

4. Analyzing and interpreting data

- *Record* observations, thoughts, and ideas.

- *Share* observations using drawings and writing.

- *Describe* patterns and relationships based on observations to answer questions or solve problems.

- *Compare* predictions to what occurred.

- *Analyze* data from tests of an object or tool to *determine* if it works as intended.

5. Using mathematics and computational thinking

- *Determine* whether to use qualitative or quantitative data.

- *Use counting* and numbers to *identify* and *describe* patterns.

- *Describe, measure,* and *compare* quantitative attributes of different objects and *display* the data using simple graphs.

- *Compare* two alternative solutions using quantitative data.

6. Constructing explanations and designing solutions

- Use observations to *construct* an evidence–based account of phenomena.

- *Design* and build a device that solves a problem.

- *Generate* and *compare* multiple solutions to a problem.

7. Engaging in argument from evidence

- *Distinguish* between explanations that account for all gathered evidence and those that do not.

- *Analyze* why some evidence is relevant and some is not.

- *Distinguish* between opinions and evidence in one's own explanation.

- *Listen actively* to arguments. *Agree* and *disagree* based on evidence; *retell the main points* of an argument.

- *Construct* and support an argument with evidence to support a claim.

- *Make a claim* about the effectiveness of an object, tool, or solution based on evidence.

8. Obtaining, evaluating, and communicating information

- *Read* to obtain scientific and technical information to determine patterns or evidence.

- *Describe* how specific images support a scientific or engineering task.

- *Obtain information* using various texts, text features, and other media to *answer questions* and *support claims.*

- *Communicate* information or design ideas/solutions orally and in writing, using models, drawings, or numbers to provide details.

Research supports the claim that when students are intentionally using language functions in thinking about and communicating in science, they improve not only science content knowledge, but also language-arts and mathematics skills (Ostlund, 1998; Lieberman and Hoody, 1998). Language functions play a central role in science as a key cognitive tool for developing higher-order thinking and problem-solving abilities that, in turn, support academic literacy in all subject areas.

Here is an example of how an experienced teacher can provide an opportunity for students to exercise language functions in FOSS. In the **Materials and Motion Module** (Kindergarten), this is one piece of content we expect students to have acquired by the end of the module.

- When objects touch or collide, they push on one another, which can change motion.

The science and engineering practices the teacher wants the class to focus on are designing solutions and analyzing and interpreting data.

The language functions students will exercise while engaging in these practices are *designing, analyzing, comparing,* and *explaining.* The teacher understands that these language functions are appropriate to the purpose of the science investigation and support the Common Core Standards for writing (students will use a combination of drawing,

▶ **NOTE**
For more examples of how FOSS teachers address language-arts standards while conducting science investigations with students, go to FOSSweb (www.FOSSweb.com).

dictating, and writing to compose explanatory texts in which they name what they are writing about and supply some information about the topic.)

Students will *compare* observational data (from a ball and ramp design challenge) to *explain* how they were able to change the direction of a ball moving down a ramp.

The teacher can support the use of language functions by providing structures such as sentence frames.

- *When I _____, then _____.*

When I put a block in the path of the ball, it went toward the pond.

SPEAKING AND LISTENING STRAND

The FOSS investigations are designed to engage students in productive oral discourse. Talking requires students to process and organize what they are learning. Listening to and evaluating peers' ideas calls on students to apply their knowledge and to sharpen their reasoning skills. Guiding students in small-group and whole-class discussions is critical to the development of conceptual understanding of the science content and the ability to think and reason scientifically. It also addresses a key Common Core Speaking and Listening standard that students "participate in collaborative discussions with diverse partners on topics and texts with peers and adults" CCSS.ELA SL1. Students' ability to engage in higher level academic discourse in science progresses as they move from kindergarten to second grade. Kindergartners begin by learning the norms for discussions and gradually become proficient at continuing a conversation through multiple exchanges. By second grade, students are effectively building on each others' ideas and asking for clarification and explanations.

FOSS investigations start with a discussion—either a review to activate prior knowledge, the presentation of a focus question, or a challenge to motivate and engage active thinking about a phenomenon. During the active investigation, students talk with one another in small groups, share their observations and discoveries, point out connections, ask questions, and start to build explanations. The discussion icon in the sidebar of the *Investigations Guide* indicates when small-group discussions should take place. These opportunities also align with the CCSS.ELA SL 4. *Describe familiar people, places, things, and events* (K-1) *recount an experience with appropriate facts and relevant details.* At various times during the investigation, students will also *ask and answer questions to clarify* (K), *gather additional information* (1st), or *deepen understanding* (2nd) *of information presented orally.* (SL2, SL3)

Throughout the activity, the *Investigations Guide* indicates where it is appropriate to pause for whole-class discussions to guide conceptual understanding. The *Investigations Guide* provides you with discussion questions to help stimulate student thinking and support sense making. At times, it may be beneficial to use sentence frames or standard prompts to scaffold the use of effective language functions and structures. Younger students can also benefit from modeling and practicing the type of language structures and vocabulary needed to communicate science and engineering ideas effectively.

At the end of the investigation, there is another opportunity to develop oral discourse skills. During the Wrap-Up/Warm-Up, students discuss their responses to the focus question and extend their understanding by

▶ NOTE
See the Sense-Making Discussions for Three-Dimensional Learning chapter for more information about planning for and supporting productive academic discourse.

connecting what they are learning to crosscutting concepts, their prior knowledge and experiences, and/or to new ideas. This is a great time to practice discussion protocols and structures such as *think-pair-share*, attentive listening, or hand-signals, and to discuss norms and expectations.

On the following pages are some suggestions for providing structure to those discussions and for scaffolding productive discourse when needed. Teaching techniques used to generate discussion in language arts and other content areas can also be used effectively during science. Using the protocols that follow will ensure inclusion of all students in discussions.

Partner and Small-Group Discussion Protocols

First and foremost, give students time to talk with a partner or in a small group before conducting a whole-class discussion. This provides all students with a chance to formulate their thinking, express their ideas, practice using the appropriate science vocabulary, and receive input from peers. Listening to others communicate different ways of thinking about the same information from a variety of perspectives helps students negotiate the difficult path of sense making for themselves.

Dyads. Students pair up and take turns either answering a question or expressing an idea. Each student has 1 minute to talk while the other student listens. While student A is talking, student B practices attentive listening. Student B makes eye contact with student A, but cannot respond verbally. After 1 minute, the roles reverse.

Here's an example from the **Solids and Liquids Module** (grade 2). Just before students answer the focus question in their notebooks, you ask students to pair up and take turns sharing their answer to the question "Is toothpaste a solid or a liquid?" The science and language learning target is for students to be able to justify their conclusions based on their observations and evidence from previous investigations (orally and in writing) that toothpaste is a mixture. A "claims and evidence" sentence frame can be written on the board to scaffold student thinking and conversation.

- I think <claim> because <the evidence>.

Partner parade. Students form two lines facing each other. Present a question, an idea, an object, or an image as a prompt for students to discuss. Give students 1 minute to greet the person in front of them and discuss the prompt. After 1 minute, call time. Have the first student in one of the lines move to the end of the line, and have the rest of the students in that line shift one step sideways so that everyone has a new partner. (Students in the other line do not move.) Give students a new prompt to discuss for 1 minute with their new partners.

Partner and Small-Group Discussion Protocols
- *Dyads*
- *Partner parade*
- *Put in your two cents*

For example, students are just beginning the investigation on weather conditions from the **Air and Weather Module** (grade 1), and you want to assess prior knowledge. Give each student a picture of a weather condition (storms, clouds, rain, snow, wind, etc.) and have students line up facing each other. For the first round, ask, "What do you think is happening in the photograph?" For the second round, ask, "What is your experience with this type of weather?" For the third round, ask, "What questions do you have?" The science and language learning target is for students to describe their observations, reflect on their own experiences with different types of weather conditions, and to ask questions about weather. The following sentence frames can be used to scaffold student discussion.

- I notice ____.

- It reminds me of ____.

- I wonder ____

Put in your two cents. For small-group discussions, give each student two pennies or similar objects to use as talking tokens. Each student takes a turn putting a penny in the center of the table and sharing his or her idea. Once all have shared, each student takes a turn putting in the other penny and responding to what others in the group have said. For example,

- I agree (or don't agree) with _____ because _____.

Here's an example from the **Pebbles, Sand, and Silt Module** (grade 2). Students have been exploring where sand comes from and are still wrestling with the idea that sand is small particles of rock. The science and language learning target is for students to describe their observations, explain how a boulder and a piece of sand can be different sizes of the same rock and provide evidence based on their own prior knowledge. You give each student two pennies, and in groups of four, they take turns putting in their two cents. For the first round, each student answers the question "Where does sand come from?" They use the frame:

- I think sand comes from ____.

- My evidence is ____.

On the second round, each student states whether he or she agrees or disagrees with someone else in the group and why, using the sentence frame. For kindergartners and first graders, you might want to start with just one round and use a "talking stick" or some other object for students to pass to each other to keep track of whose turn it is to speak.

Whole-Class Discussion Supports
- *Sentence frames*
- *Guiding questions*

Whole-Class Discussion Supports

The whole-class discussion is a critical part of sense making. After students have had the active learning experience and have talked with their peers in partners and/or small groups, sharing their observations with the whole class sets the stage for developing conventional explanatory models. Discrepant events, differing results, and other surprises are discussed, analyzed, and resolved. It is important that students realize that science is a process of finding out about the world around them. This is done through asking questions, testing ideas, forming explanations, and subjecting those explanations to logical scrutiny. Leading students through productive discussion helps them connect their observations and the abstract symbols (words) that represent and explain those observations. Whole-class discussions also provide opportunities for you to prompt student thinking with questions and to interject missing pieces of information they may need to consider to come to accurate conclusions. You might also need to model the kind of discourse and thinking processes you expect from your students. Facilitating effective whole-class discussions takes skill, practice, a shared set of norms, and patience. In the long run, students will have a better grasp of the content and will be better at thinking independently and communicating more effectively. See the Sense-Making Discussions for Three-Dimensional Learning chapter for additional resources.

Norms should be introduced, modeled, and practiced so that students know what is expected during science discussions. Start with one or two at a time and be sure to discuss why norms are important and have students reflect on how well they adhere to them.

- We stay on the topic of science.
- Everyone participates.
- We share our own ideas and experiences and respect those of others.
- We explain our ideas.
- We ask others to explain or repeat if we don't understand.

The same discussion techniques used during ELA and other whole-class discussions can be used during science instruction (e.g., attentive listening, staying focused on the speaker, asking questions, responding appropriately). In addition, in order for students to develop and practice their reasoning skills, they need to know the language forms and structures and the behaviors used in argumentation [e.g., using data to support claims, disagreeing respectfully, asking probing questions (Winokur and Worth, 2006)].

TEACHING NOTE

Let students know that scientists change their minds based on new evidence. It is expected that students will revise their thinking based on evidence presented in discussions.

Explicitly model and conduct mini-lessons (5 to 10 minutes of focused instruction) on the language structures appropriate for active discussions, and provide time for students to practice them, using the science and engineering content.

Sentence frames. The following samples can be posted as a scaffold as students learn and practice their reasoning and oral participation skills.

- I think _____, because _____.
- I predict _____, because _____.
- I claim _____; my evidence is _____.
- I agree with _____ that _____.
- My idea is similar/related to _____'s idea.
- I learned/discovered/heard that _____.
- <Name> explained _____ to me.
- <Name> shared _____ with me.
- We decided/agreed that _____.
- Our group sees it differently, because _____.
- We have different observations/results. Some of us found that _____. One group member thinks that _____.
- We had a different approach/idea/solution/answer _____.

Guiding questions. The *Investigations Guide* provides questions to help concentrate student thinking on the concepts introduced in the investigation. Guiding questions should be used during the whole-class discussion to facilitate sense making. Here are some other open-ended questions that help guide student thinking and promote discussion.

- What did you notice when _____?
- What do you think will happen if _____?
- How might you explain _____? What is your evidence?
- What connections can you make between _____ and _____?

If you are having trouble understanding or following a student's line of thinking, ask questions like:

- Can you say more about that?
- Can someone else respond to what <Name> just said?
- Are you saying ___?

> **TEACHING NOTE**
>
> *Allow time for students to engage in discussions that build on other students' observations and reasoning. After an investigation, use a teacher- or student-generated question, and either just listen or facilitate the interaction with questions to encourage expression of ideas among students.*

Whole-Class Discussion Protocols

- *Think-pair-share*
- *Pick a stick*
- *Whip around*
- *Group posters*

Two-cup pick-a-stick container

One-cup pick-a-stick container divided with tape

Whole-Class Discussion Protocols

The following examples of tried-and-true participation protocols can be used to enhance whole-class discussions during science and all other curriculum areas. The purpose of these protocols is to increase meaningful participation by giving all students access to the discussion, allowing students time to think (process), and providing a context for motivation and engagement.

Think-pair-share. When asking for a response to a question posed to the class, allow time for students to think silently for a minute. Then, have students pair up with a partner to exchange thoughts before you call on a student to share his or her ideas with the whole class. Variations include having one partner paraphrase what the other said or giving students the option of sharing what their partner said.

Pick a stick. Write each student's name on a craft stick, and keep the sticks handy at the front of the room. When asking for responses, randomly pick a stick, and call on that student to start the discussion. Continue to select sticks as you continue the discussion. Your name can also be on a stick in the cup. You can put the selected sticks in a different location or back into the same cup to be selected again.

Whip around. Each student takes a quick turn sharing a thought or reaction. Questions are phrased to elicit quick responses that can be expressed in one to five words (e.g., "Give an example of a type of tree." "What are some things that make a sound?").

Group posters. Have small groups design and graphically record their investigation data, their models, or conclusions on a quickly generated poster to share with the whole class.

Hand signals. Nonverbal signals can be used to encourage all class participation in discussions. For example, students can show with their hands whether they agree or disagree with a statement, if they want to add on to an idea, or if they have a question. Be sure to model how to use signals appropriately so they are not a distraction for the student speaking.

WRITING STRAND

Information processing is enhanced when students engage in informal writing. When allowed to write expressively without fear of being scorned for incorrect spelling or grammar, students are more apt to organize and express their thoughts in different ways that support sense making. Writing in science promotes the use of science and engineering practices, thereby developing a deeper engagement with the disciplinary core ideas and the crosscutting concepts. This type of informal writing also provides a springboard for more formal derivative science writing (Keys, 1999).

Science Notebooks

The science notebook is an effective tool for enhancing learning in science and developing writing skills. Notebooks provide opportunities both for expressive writing and drawing (students craft explanatory narratives and pictures that make sense of their science experiences) and for learning and practicing informal technical writing (students use organizational structures and writing conventions). Starting as emergent writers in kindergarten, students learn to communicate their thinking in an organized fashion while engaging in the cognitive processes required to develop concepts and build explanations. Having this developmental record of learning provides an authentic means for assessing students' progress in both scientific thinking and communication skills. Using notebooks also supports the Common Core Writing standards, e.g., students (*with guidance* K-1) *recall information from experiences to answer a question* (W8), *write* (or *draw/dictate* K) *opinions and supply a reason and conclusion* (W1), *write* (or *draw/dictate* K) *explanatory texts with concluding statements* (W2), *write* (or *draw/dictate*) *narratives using event sequence* (W3), and *develop and strengthen writing with guidance and support from adults* (W5).

One way to help students develop the writing skills necessary for productive notebook entries is to focus on the corresponding language functions. The language forms and structures used to perform these language functions in science are used in all curricular areas and, therefore, can be suitably taught in conjunction with existing language-arts instruction. This can be done through mini-lessons on the writing skills that support the various types of notebook entries.

Table 1, at the end of the Writing Strand section, provides examples of how language functions are used to help students develop both their general writing skills and their thinking abilities within the format of the science-notebook entry. The writing objectives for a mini-lesson, along with the particular language forms and structures (vocabulary, syntax, linking words, organization of ideas, and so on), are identified in the table along with the suggested sentence frames for scaffolding.

> **▶ NOTE**
> For more information about supporting science-notebook development, see the Science Notebooks chapter.

> **▶ NOTE**
> Language forms and structures refer to the internal grammatical structure of words and how those words go together to make sentences.

For example, in the **Insects and Plants Module** (grade 2) when students are observing a mealworms' behavior, the literacy-learning target might be "Students use temporal words to describe the behavior of the mealworm." A prior mini-lesson on using linking words and phrases to describe observations would provide students with the language forms and structures appropriate for recording their data in their notebooks during the observations. As a scaffold, students could also be provided with temporal words and phrases to help them write detailed narratives.

▶ **NOTE**
The complete table appears at the end of this Writing Strand section.

Language function	Language objectives for writing in notebooks	Language forms, structures, and scaffolds for writing
Notebook component—data acquisition		
Describe	Write narratives to develop real experience; use descriptive details and clear event sequencing. (CCSS.ELA W3)	I observed ___. When I touch the ___, I feel ___. The ___ has ___. I noticed ___. It feels ___. It smells ___. It sounds ___. It reminds me of ___, because ___.

This sample from Table 1 shows how language functions can be developed and applied when writing in science notebooks.

Derivative Language-Arts Products
- *Argumentation writing*
- *Informative/explanatory writing*
- *Narrative writing*

TEACHING NOTE

Creation of derivative products as well as more formal writing instruction can be done during language arts time.

Developing Derivative Language-Arts Products

Science notebooks provide students with a source of information (content) from which they can draw to create more formal science-centered writing pieces. Derivative products are written pieces that are generated with specific language-arts goals in mind, such as purpose, text types, and audience. Writing-to-learn methods can enhance science concepts when students engage in different types of writing for different purposes (Hand and Prain, 2002). We know that students are more engaged and motivated to write when they have a clear and authentic context for writing.

The language extensions in the Interdisciplinary Extensions section at the end of each investigation suggest writing activities that can be used to help students learn the science content for that particular investigation. The writing activities incorporate language-arts skills appropriate for the grade level. Questions and ideas for future writing activities that surface during the investigations can be recorded in a class list, in science notebooks, or in students' writing folders. Here are general suggestions for using science content to create products in each of several writing genres including those addressed in the Common Core for English Language Arts (CCSS.ELA).

Argumentation Writing

The CCSS for ELA define an argument as *a reasoned, logical way of demonstrating that the writer's position, belief, or conclusion is valid. In science, students make claims in the form of statements or conclusions that answer questions or address problems. Using data in a scientifically acceptable form, students marshal evidence and draw on their understanding of scientific concepts to argue in support of their claims.* Across the disciplines, students write arguments to either 1) change a point of view, 2) bring about some type of action, or 3) put forth an explanation or evaluation of a concept, issue, or problem. For K–5 students, this type of writing is called an "opinion piece." The term "opinion" is used to refer to a developing form of argument (CCSS for ELA/Literacy Appendix A). For grades K–2, students *introduce a topic or text, state an opinion* (K), and *supply a reason for the opinion and provide a conclusion* (1-2)

Engaging in argument from evidence in the FOSS investigations supports this type of writing. Use the questions and prompts in the *Investigations Guide* that encourage students to use their observations, models, and information from the text or multimedia to support both their oral and written arguments. In addition, be prepared for those teachable moments that provide the perfect stage for spontaneous scientific debate. Here are some general questions to help students strengthen their argumentation writing.

- Why do you think that ___?
- Do you agree or disagree with ___? Why?
- Which do you think is better? Why?
- Why was it better that ___?

Following are more ways engaging in written argument are developed in the FOSS investigations and can be extended through formal writing.

Answer the focus question. When answering the focus question, students make a claim (or state their opinion) and provide evidence to support their claim based on their observations from the investigation and patterns they can identify. This is usually in the form of "I think _____ (claim) because _____ (evidence)." Students can revisit their responses, add a line of learning, and revise their claim or add new evidence. For formal writing, have students use the information from their notebooks to expand on their response in a more polished opinion piece that includes more detailed illustrations, linking words, and a concluding statement. (W1)

Thinking about questions. Interactive reading in *FOSS Science Resources* is another opportunity for students to engage in written argumentation. Articles include questions that support reading comprehension and extend student thinking about the science content. Asking students to make a claim and provide evidence to support it, encourages the use of language functions necessary for higher-level thinking such as evaluating, applying, and justifying. For example, in the **Sound and Light** *FOSS Science Resources* (grade1), students are asked to think about reflections. *How is a shadow different from a reflection?*

I-Checks and Surveys/Posttests (grades 1–2). Included in the assessments are items that assess students' ability to make a claim and provide evidence to support it. One way is to provide students with data and have them make a claim based on that data and evidence from their prior investigations. Their argument should use logical reasoning to support their ideas. For example, in the **Pebbles, Sand, and Silt Module** (grade 2) students are presented with two ways to make sand castle towers. Based on their experiences with sand and matrix, they predict what will happen to the two structures.

Persuasive writing. Opportunities to practice writing in their notebooks builds the foundation for the more formal writing students will be asked to do in the upper grades. Students learn to record their observations, explain, and apply their emerging science knowledge. Sharing their writing and drawings with an audience also motivates students to produce higher-level writing products. The objective of persuasive writing is to convince the reader that a stated interpretation of data is worthwhile and meaningful. Students learn to support their claims with evidence and how to use persuasive techniques such as a call to action. Through interactive, shared, or scaffolded independent writing students can draw on the information from their investigations to jointly craft persuasive writing in a variety of formats, such as, posters, letters, advertisements, informational pamphlets, and petitions. Animal habitats, energy use, weather patterns, landforms, and water sources are just a few science topics that can generate questions and issues for persuasive writing.

Here is an example of a persuasive writing frame for an opinion piece,

We think that _____ .

The reasons are _____ and _____ .

For these reasons we think _____ .

Informative/Explanatory Writing

Informational and explanatory writing requires students to examine and convey ideas and information clearly. Described in CCSS. ELA Appendix A, informational/explanatory writing answers the questions, *What type? What are the parts? What are the properties, functions, and behaviors? How does it work? What is happening? Why?* In FOSS, this type of writing takes place informally in science notebooks, where students are recording their questions, plans, procedures, data, models, and explanations. It also supports sense making as students attempt to convey what they know in response to questions and prompts, using language functions such as identifying, comparing and contrasting, explaining cause-and-effect relationships, and sequencing.

During writing instruction, students can use the information in their science notebooks and in related readings (and other sources, such as video content) to write a more formal and conclusive answer to the focus question in the form of an explanatory text by introducing a topic, using facts and definitions to develop points, and providing a concluding statement (W2).

Students can also apply their science knowledge to inform, explain, clarify, define, or instruct through writing letters, definitions, procedures, newspaper and magazine articles, blogs, posters, pamphlets, and research reports. Strategies such as the writing process (plan, draft, edit, revise, and share) and writing frames (modeling and guiding the use of topic sentences, transition and sequencing words, examples, explanations, and conclusions) can be used to scaffold and help students develop proficiency in informative/explanatory writing.

Here are two samples of writing frames.

Living Structures

Title: _____

(Identify) The parts of the _____ I observe are the _____ , _____ , and the _____ .

(Describe) The _____ is for _____ . The _____ is for _____ .

(Explain) Together, they _____ .

(Example) This drawing shows _____ .

Explanations

Title: _____

I want to explain why (how) _____ .

The reason is _____ .

Another reason is that _____.

I know this because _____.

> **TEACHING NOTE**
>
> *When students use organisms for scientific informational writing, have a conversation about the difference between fiction and nonfiction, e.g., animals don't talk or drive cars.*

NOTE
Human characteristics should
not be given to organisms
(anthropomorphism) in science
investigations, only in literacy
extensions.

Narrative Writing

Narrative writing conveys an experience to the reader, usually with sensory detail and a sequence of events. In science, kindergarteners use a combination of drawing, dictating, and writing to narrate what they did and observed during the investigation in the order in which they occurred and their reaction. Second and third graders include more and more detail, describe actions, use temporal words, and provide a sense of closure. Writing and drawing routinely in their notebooks allows student to practice this type of writing informally. They can also use the context of the FOSS investigations to write more formal narrative pieces to describe the sequence of events and their thoughts and feelings (CCSS.ELA W3).

Science provides a broad landscape of engaging material for stimulating the imagination for the writing of stories, songs, chants, poems, and skits. Students can use organisms or objects as characters; describe habitats and environments as settings; and write scripts portraying various systems, such as weather patterns, the story of a rock, or life cycles.

Descriptive writing. Students use descriptive writing to portray an organism, an environment, an object, or a phenomenon. They learn to use sensory language and vivid and lively details.

To help them extend their learning of the disciplinary core ideas, students can use the information in their science notebooks to elaborate on their observations by using descriptive vocabulary, temporal words and phrases, and drawing.

Kindergarteners can dictate their observations or contribute to a class notebook describing animals, trees, landforms, wood, etc.

First and second graders can make property cards by writing on an index card as many properties as they can that describe an object or organism. Then, students take turns reading the properties to another student to see if the partner can identify the corresponding object.

Table 1. Examples of how language functions are exercised in science notebook writing and examples of sentence frames and language structures teachers can model and students may use as they develop their writing skills

Language function	Language objectives for writing in notebooks	Language forms, structures, and scaffolds for writing
Organizational setup		
Organize	Set up and organize notebook: table of contents (for grade 2), page numbers, date, turning to the next blank page.	Model using a classroom notebook. Use structures such as rows, columns, blocks, numbers, location, alphabetizing.
Notebook component—planning the investigation		
Design Strategize	Write a narrative plan: communicate ideas on an approach to answer the focus question or challenge posed in the investigation.	Use adverbs such as *first, second, next, then, finally.* Brainstorming ideas: First I will ____, and then I will ____. I will need to ____ to ____.
List Record	Write ordered lists: materials, variables, vocabulary words, bullets	We need ____, ____, ____, and ____ to ____.
Sequence	Record procedures: number steps in a sequence.	1. _____. 2. _____. 3. _____. I will observe ____. I will measure ____.
Notebook component—data acquisition		
Describe	Write narratives: use details, sensory observations, connections to prior knowledge.	I observed ____. When I touch the ____, I feel ____. The ____ has ____. I noticed ____. It feels ____. It smells ____. It sounds ____. It reminds me of ____, because ____.

Table 1 (*continued*)

Language function	Language objectives for writing in notebooks	Language forms, structures, and scaffolds for writing
Notebook component—data acquisition (continued)		
Draw Label Identify	Make technical drawings: draw large, accurate, and detailed representations; identify parts of a system.	Label drawing, using science vocabulary. Recognize shapes, form, location, color, size, and scale. My drawing shows ____.
Organize Compare Classify	Make charts and tables: use a T-table or chart for recording and displaying data.	Set up rows, columns, headings. My T-table compares ____.
Sequence Compare	Record changes: use language structures to communicate change over time, cause and effect.	At first, ____, but now ____. We saw that first ____, then ____, and finally ____. When I ____, it ____. After I ____, it ____.
Notebook component—data organization		
Enumerate	Decide when to use qualitative vs. quantitative data; use counting and numbers to identify patterns; describe, measure, and compare quantitative attributes of different objects; display data using simple graphs.	We counted ____. We measured ____. There are more/less ____. The __ is bigger/smaller____. We found out that ____. The graph/table shows____
Compare Classify Sequence	Use graphic organizers and narratives to express similarities and differences, to assign an object or action to the category or type to which it belongs, and to show sequencing and order.	This ____ is the same as ____ because ____. This ____ is different than ____ because ____. All these are ____ because ____. ____, ____, and ____ all have/are ____.
Analyze	Use graphic organizers, narratives or concept maps to identify part/whole or cause–and–effect relationships.	Use relationship verbs such as *are made of, are part of*. As ____, then ____. When I changed ____, then ____ happened. The more/less ____, then ____.

Table 1 (*continued*)

Language function	Language objectives for writing in notebooks	Language forms, structures, and scaffolds for writing
Notebook component—sense-making		
Infer Explain	Provide claims and evidence: write conclusions about what was learned from the investigation, use the data (observations) as evidence to support those claims.	Use inferential logical connectors such as *but, even though*. I claim that ____. I know this because ____.
Provide evidence	Use qualitative and quantitative data from the investigation as evidence to support claims.	Use qualitative descriptors such as *more/less, longer/shorter, higher/lower*. Use quantitative expressions using standard metric units of measurement such as cm. I measured ____. I observed ____.
Summarize Predict Generalize	Write a summary narrative to communicate what was learned; ask questions and make predictions based on the newly acquired knowledge.	Answer the focus question by rewriting it as a statement and providing evidence from observations. Make a concluding statement. I learned ____. I think ____. I predict ____ because ____.
Notebook component—next-step strategies		
Critique Evaluate	Reflect on experience: review notebook entries and revise, use line of learning to revise.	I used to think ____, but now I think ____. I have changed my thinking about ____. I am confused about ____ because ____. I wonder ____.

▶ **CCSS NOTE**

Asking and answering questions, identifying the main topic and key details, and making connections address the CCSS for ELA RI 1-3.

READING STRAND

Reading is an integral part of science learning. Just as scientists spend a significant amount of their time reading one another's published works, students need to learn to read scientific text—to read effectively for understanding with a critical focus on the ideas being presented.

The articles in *FOSS Science Resources* help facilitate sense making as students make connections to the science concepts introduced and explored during the active investigations. Concept development is most effective when students are allowed to experience organisms, objects, and phenomena firsthand before engaging the concepts in text. The text and illustrations help students make connections between what they have experienced concretely and the abstract ideas that explain their observations.

FOSS Science Resources supports developing literacy skills by providing reading material that corresponds exactly to the concrete, personal experience provided in the active investigations. Students read with enthusiasm when they recognize familiar materials, organisms, and activities and are eager to tackle the reading to confirm their prior knowledge and discover more about the topic. In addition to making connections, once engaged, students naturally use other reading-comprehension strategies, such as asking questions, visualizing, inferring, and synthesizing, to help them understand the reading. As students apply these strategies, they are, in effect, using some of the same scientific thinking processes that promote critical thinking and problem solving.

Learning to Read Informational Texts

In the kindergarten modules, you can enhance science learning by using trade books and other read-aloud resources to engage students and provide topics for lively discussions. Reading aloud helps primary students understand the science content and lets you model reading comprehension strategies, such as asking yourself questions (thinking aloud) and summarizing a paragraph just read. The reading in *FOSS Science Resources* sections offer suggestions for activating prior knowledge before reading, indicate places to pause and discuss key points during the reading, and describe activities to deepen understanding after the reading. As students develop their reading skills, you might try these different ways to read from *FOSS Science Resources*.

- Read aloud from the big book while students follow along in their own books.
- Lead students in small guided reading groups.
- Have students read aloud with a partner.
- Have students read silently on their own.

The same strategies used in language arts to address the CCSS.ELA RI 10 can be applied to reading in science. Kindergartners are actively engaged in group reading activities to find out more about their science investigations; first graders begin to access the complex text found in the *FOSS Science Resources* articles with prompting and support; and second graders read and comprehend the articles with scaffolding as needed (CCSS.ELA RI 10).

Build on background knowledge. Activating prior knowledge is critical for helping students make connections between what they already know and new information. Reading comprehension improves when students have the opportunity to think about and discuss what they know about a topic before reading. Review what students learned from the active investigation, provide prompts for making connections, and ask questions to help students recall past experiences and previous exposure to concepts related to the reading. Ask students to discuss the photographs and diagrams and how they relate to the written text. They should ask themselves: *What do I know about this picture? What don't I know? What does it remind me of? I wonder...* As they listen to or read the text on their own, remind them to think back on their original interpretations to see if they match those of the author.

Model close reading. Begin with reading the article aloud so that students can hear the content read fluently and listen for meaning and coherence. Go back and review the questions and prompts within the article. Use think-pair-share or other discussion protocols to allow students to think first, share with a partner, and then respond to the group. For kindergartners and beginning readers, emphasize blending phonemes as you read the text again, and model tracking, connecting spoken words with written words, and helping students identify sight words. Model reading-comprehension strategies by using think-alouds (as you think aloud, you explain the process that you are using in order to understand the text while reading).

Examine craft and structure. The expository text structure of the articles provides the opportunity for primary students to learn how to extract information from a table of contents, a glossary, an index, and other text conventions such as headings, subheads, boldface and italic print, labeled graphics, and captions. (CCSS.ELA RI 5 *know and use text features.*) They can also practice *asking and answering questions to clarify word meanings* (RI 4 K-1) and *use strategies for determining the meaning of unknown words and phrases such as sentence level context clues, prefixes and root words, and glossaries* (RI 4 and L4 grade 2).

Building reading comprehension skills. When appropriate, use the articles to point out and discuss with students important features to consider when reading informational text, such *as how the illustrations relate to and help them to understand the key ideas* in the articles (CCSS. ELA RI 7) and *the reasons the author gives to support specific points* (RI 8). Students can also *compare the information in the FOSS Science Resources* book articles *with other texts of the same topic* (RI 9). At the end of articles, use the questions provided to guide understanding and to assess comprehension and vocabulary acquisition. For second graders you might choose one or two questions for them to answer in their notebooks. Emphasize the importance of science vocabulary and the appropriate language forms and structures. Here are some ways students can enhance reading comprehension.

- Have students predict the sequence of events or content.
- Have students write or dictate questions about the text and illustrations.
- Use visualization with students to "see, touch, feel, smell, hear" in their minds the content presented in the article.
- Ask students to make connections between their observations during the active investigation and the information in the article.

SCIENCE-VOCABULARY DEVELOPMENT

Words play two critically important functions in science. First and most important, we play with ideas in our minds, using words. We present ourselves with propositions—possibilities, questions, potential relationships, implications for action, and so on. The process of sorting out these thoughts involves a lot of internal conversation, internal argument, weighing of options, and complex linguistic decisions. Once our minds are made up, communicating that decision, conclusion, or explanation in writing or through verbal discourse requires the same command of the vocabulary. Words represent intelligence; acquiring the precise vocabulary and the associated meanings is key to successful scientific thinking and communication.

The words introduced in FOSS investigations represent or relate to fundamental science concepts and should be taught in the context of the investigation. Many of the terms are abstract and are critical to developing science content knowledge and scientific and engineering practices. The goal is for students to use science vocabulary in ways that demonstrate understanding of the concepts the words represent— not to merely recite scripted definitions. The most effective science-vocabulary development strategies help students make connections to what they already know. These strategies focus on giving new words conceptual meaning through experience; distinguishing between informal, everyday language and academic language; and using the words in meaningful contexts.

Building Conceptual Meaning through Experience

In most instances, students should be presented with new words in the context of the active experience at the need-to-know point in the investigation. Words such as *vibration, weathering, dissolve, evaporate, variation,* and *larva* are conceptually loaded and significantly abstract. Students will have a much better chance of understanding, assimilating, and remembering the new word (or new meaning) if they can connect it with a concrete experience.

Say it

Write it

New Word

See it

Hear it

The new-word icon appears in the sidebar when you introduce a word that is critical to understanding the concepts or scientific practices students will be learning and applying in the investigation. When you introduce a new word, students should

- Hear it: Students listen as you model the correct contextual use and pronunciation of the word.

- See it: Students see the new word written out. Add a visual reference (an illustration or a sample) next to the word if possible.

- Say it: Have students say the word chorally and clap out the syllables.

- Write it: You write the word on the board, chart paper, sentence strip, or card. Students use the new words in context when they write in their notebooks.

- Act it: Demonstrate action words such as *separate*, *compare*, and *observe* (using total physical response).

Bridging Informal Language to Science Vocabulary

Students bring a wealth of language experience to the classroom. FOSS investigations are designed to tap into students' inquisitive natures and their excitement of discovery in order to encourage lively discussions as they explore materials in creative ways. There should be a lot of talking during science time! Your role is to help students connect informal language to the vocabulary used to express specific science concepts. As you circulate during active investigation, you continually model the use of science vocabulary. Following are some strategies for validating students' conversational language while developing their familiarity with and appreciation for science vocabulary.

Word bubbles. Choose a word from the word wall that is widely used by students and that is a synonym for a science vocabulary word. Draw a circle on the board or chart paper, and write the word in the center. Draw lines out from the circled word, and make more circles. Ask students to call out more synonyms for the word, and write them in the outer circles. Introduce the target vocabulary word as yet one more synonym for the target word, a word that is used in science. Highlight the word, and model its correct usage and pronunciation. Encourage students to use it in their discussions and in their notebook entries. Introduce the science word that is its opposite, when appropriate.

Word sorts. Make a set of word cards from words on the word wall. Ask students to help you group the words that are synonyms or that have conceptual connections. Add the new science words to the card set. Repeat the process with a new set of words. For advanced students, make sets of vocabulary cards for them to sort with a partner or in small groups.

Bridging Language Strategies
- *Word bubbles*
- *Word sorts*
- *Semantic webs*
- *Concept maps*
- *Cognitive content dictionaries*
- *Word associations*

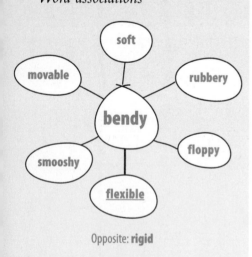

Opposite: **rigid**

Word bubbles

▶ **CCSS NOTE**

These strategies address the CCSS for ELA Language Strand, Vocabulary Acquisition and Use, 4-6.

Semantic webs. Select a vocabulary word, and write it in the center of a piece of paper (or on the board if doing this with the whole class). Brainstorm a list of words or ideas that are related to the first word. Group the words and concepts into several categories, and attach them to the central word with lines, forming a web (modified from Hamilton, 2002).

Concept maps. Select six to ten related science words and write them on self-stick notes or cards. Place them on the board and have students help you organize them into groups. When the class agrees on a way to organize the words, draw lines between the related words. On the lines, write connecting words that describe or explain how the concept words are related. Once students are familiar with the process they can work together in small groups to make their own concept maps.

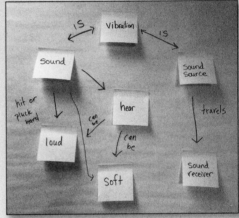

A concept map to develop vocabulary about sound

Cognitive content dictionaries. There are a variety of frameworks to help students record their learning of new words. This example can be used with the whole class or individually to introduce a few key vocabulary words used in an investigation. Write the word on the board or chart paper, ask students to predict its meaning, write the final meaning after class discussion, and then use the word in a sentence. The word can also be used as a signal word to call for attention.

Cognitive Content Dictionary	
New word	tundra
Prediction (clues)	a really dry place
Final meaning	a place in the artic or high on the mountains
How I would use it (sentence)	The artic fox lives in the tundra where it is cold.

Word associations. In this brainstorming activity, you say a word, and students respond by sharing the first word that comes to mind. Generate a list of words based on students' responses. This activity builds connections to students' prior frames of reference.

▶ CCSS NOTE

These strategies address the CCSS for ELA Language Strand, Vocabulary Acquisition and Use, 4-6.

L4 Determine the meaning of unknown words and phrases

L5 Demonstrate understanding of word relationships and nuances

L6 Use acquired words and phrases.

Using Science Vocabulary in Context

In order for a new vocabulary word to become part of a student's functional vocabulary, he or she must have ample opportunities to hear and use it. The use of vocabulary terms is embedded throughout the entire investigation through discussions, during investigations, writing in science notebooks, readings, assessments, interactive media, and games. In addition, other methods used during language-arts instruction can be used to *reinforce* important vocabulary words and phrases.

Word wall/word cards. Use chart paper or a pocket chart to record both science content and procedural words. Record the words as they come up during and after the investigations. Then copy key words on sentence strips or cards, and put them in a pocket chart. With a pocket chart, words can be sorted and moved around easily. For example, you could ask students to find words that are synonyms, antonyms, nouns, or verbs. Word cards should be available to each group during the investigation. This allows students to retrieve a word quickly when they are labeling diagrams and objects used during the investigation.

Drawings and diagrams. For English learners and visual learners, a diagram can be used to review and explain abstract content. Ahead of time, draw an illustration lightly, almost invisibly, with pencil on chart paper. When it's time for the investigation, trace the illustration with markers as you introduce the words and phrases to students. Students will be amazed by your artistic ability.

Pictorial of a meteorologist used in
Air and Weather Module

Cloze activities. Structure a sentence for students to complete, leaving out the vocabulary word, and crafting the sentence so that the missing vocabulary word is the last word in the sentence. You can do this chorally or in writing on the board or chart paper. Here's an example from the **Solids and Liquids Module**.

> Teacher: *Liquids that are clear and that you can see through are _____.*
>
> Students: *Transparent.*

Word wizard. Tell students that you are going to lead a word activity. You will be thinking of a science vocabulary word from the word wall. The goal is to figure out the word. Provide hints that have to do with parts of a definition, root word, prefix, suffix, and other relevant components. Students work in teams of two to four. Provide one hint, and give teams 1 minute to discuss. One team member writes the word on a piece of paper or on the whiteboard, using dark marking pens. Each team holds up its word for only you to see. After the third clue, reveal the word, and move on to the next word.

> 1. *This word is part of a plant.*
>
> 2. *It is usually not green.*
>
> 3. *It brings water and nutrients into the plant.*
>
> *It is the* **root**.

Word analysis/word parts. Learning clusters of words that share a common origin can help students understand content-area texts and connect new words to familiar ones. This type of contextualized teaching meets the immediate need of understanding an unknown word while building generative knowledge that supports students in figuring out difficult words for future reading.

> *geology*
>
> *geologist*
>
> *geological*
>
> *geography*
>
> *geometry*
>
> *geophysical*

Reading. After the active investigation, students continue to develop their understanding of the vocabulary words and the concepts those words represent by listening to you read aloud, reading with a partner, or reading independently. Use strategies discussed in the Reading Informational Texts section to encourage students to articulate their thoughts and practice the new vocabulary.

Games. The informal activities included in the investigations are designed to reinforce important vocabulary words. Once students learn them, the words can be integrated into any type of independent work time, such as centers, workshops, and early-finisher tasks.

ENGLISH-LANGUAGE DEVELOPMENT

Active investigations provide an optimal learning environment for English learners (ELs) to develop and use language in meaningful ways. This section highlights the English-language development (ELD) opportunities inherent in the FOSS lesson design and suggests additional scaffolds, modifications, and linguistic accommodations that support student engagement in the science and engineering practices as well as the development of academic literacy. Our starting point is the hands-on collaborative structure of FOSS investigations, which is essential for both the conceptual development of science content knowledge and the habits of mind that guide and define the science and engineering practices. Students are engaged in concrete experiences with phenomena and challenging tasks that provide a shared context for interacting in meaningful ways to developing understanding—a critical component for developing language proficiency. The WIDA (World-class Instructional Design and Assessment) and ELP Standards (English Language Proficiency Standards with Correspondences to the K-12 Practices and Common Core State, Council of Chief State School Officers) and other similar state standards all stress the importance of engaging ELs in authentic, meaningful, and rigorous tasks that require constructing meaning through collaborative exchanges of information. The ELPS are organized into three modalities of communication receptive (listening and reading); productive (speaking and writing); and interactive (collaboration using receptive and productive).

Another critical component for ELD in science is strategic scaffolding—both planned and "just-in-time." To address the needs of English learners, the *Investigations Guide* includes EL notes at points in the investigations where students at beginning levels of English proficiency may need additional supports. When getting ready for an investigation, review the EL notes, and determine the points where differentiated instruction for ELs is needed or where the whole class might benefit from additional language development supports. It is helpful to consider these needs in terms of all three modes of communication—receptive, productive, and interactive. In other words, ask yourself, *What will be challenging for my students when **listening** to others and **reading** the FOSS Sciences Resources? What kind of support will they need to **write** a response to the focus question or to **speak** in the sense-making discussion? How will I make sure students are **including everyone** in their small-group tasks?*

> **NOTE**
> English-language development refers to the advancement of students' ability to read, write, and speak English.

> **NOTE**
> See Table 1 for ways that the FOSS Instructional design provides opportunities to address the WIDA and ELPS.

EL NOTE
Look for EL notes in the investigations at points where students at beginning levels of English proficiency may need additional support.

One way to plan for ELD integration and science instruction is to keep in mind four key areas: activating students' prior knowledge, ensuring comprehensible input, developing academic language, and providing for oral practice. The ELD chart below lists examples of universal strategies for each of these areas that are effective for science instruction for ELs and align with the WIDA, ELPS, and other state standards.

English-Language Development (ELD) Quadrants	
Activating prior knowledge	**Using comprehensible input**
• Inquiry chart • Circle map • Observation poster • Quick write • Kit inventory	• Content objectives • Multiple exposures • Visual aids • Supported reading • Procedural vocabulary
Developing academic language	**Providing oral practice**
• Language objectives • Sentence frames • Word wall, word cards, drawings • Concept maps • Cognitive content dictionaries	• Small-group discussions • Science talk • Oral presentations • Poems, chants, and songs • Teacher feedback

Activating Prior Knowledge

When an investigation presents a new phenomenon or concept, first students recall and discuss familiar situations, objects, or experiences that relate to and establish a foundation for building new knowledge and conceptual understanding. Eliciting prior knowledge supports learning by motivating interest, acknowledging culture and values, and checking for alternative or incomplete explanations and prerequisite knowledge. This way of engaging students is usually done in the first steps of Guiding the Investigation in the form of an oral discussion or presentation of new materials. The Letter to Family and the Home/School Connection activities also provide opportunities to tap into students' cultural and linguistic knowledge. In addition, the tools outlined below can be used before beginning an investigation to establish a familiar context for launching into new material.

Circle maps. Draw two concentric circles on chart paper. In the middle circle, write the topic to be explored. In the second circle, record what students already know about the subject. Ask students to think about how they know or learned what they already know about the topic. Record the responses outside the circles.

Strategies for Activating Prior Knowledge

- *Circle maps*
- *Observation posters*
- *Quick writes*
- *Kit inventories*
- *Letter to Family*
- *Home/School Connections*

▶ **ELPS NOTE**
These strategies address all three modalities (receptive, productive, and interactive) in the ELPS 1-3; WIDA standard 4.

An example of a circle map

We used magnets in kindergarten to sort materials for recycling.

We have lots of magnets on our refrigerator at home.

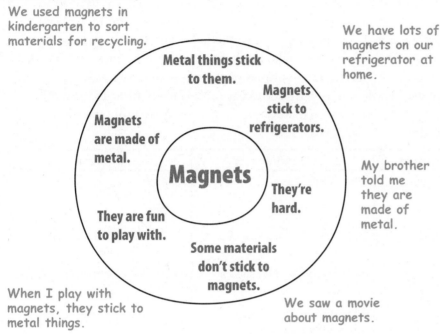

Metal things stick to them.

Magnets stick to refrigerators.

Magnets are made of metal.

Magnets

They're hard.

My brother told me they are made of metal.

They are fun to play with.

Some materials don't stick to magnets.

When I play with magnets, they stick to metal things.

We saw a movie about magnets.

Observation posters. Make observation posters by gluing or taping pictures and artifacts relevant to the module or a particular investigation onto pieces of blank chart paper or poster paper. Try to include images that relate to students' cultural and linguistic identities and interests. Hang them on the walls in the classroom, and have students rotate in small groups to each poster. At each station, students discuss their observations with their partners or small groups and then record or dictate an observation, a question, a prediction, or an inference about the pictures as a contribution to the commentary on the poster.

First grade students write about weather.

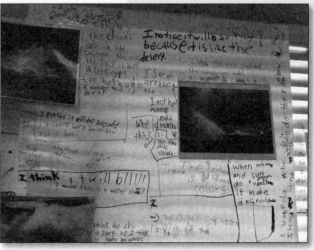

An observation poster from the Air and Weather Module

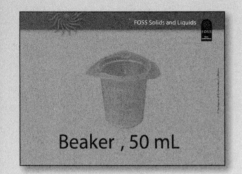

Beaker , 50 mL

Kit inventories. Introduce each item from the FOSS kit used in the investigation, and ask students questions to get them thinking about what each item is and where they may have seen it before. Have them describe the objects and make predictions about how they will be used in the investigation. Tape samples of the items on chart paper, or print and display the equipment photo cards (download from FOSSweb) along with the name and a description, to serve as an interactive word wall.

Item	Teacher	Student
Bottle	What is this?	A bottle.
	What is it made of?	Plastic.
	What is it used for?	To hold liquids.
Scoop	What is this?	It looks like a spoon.
	It's like a spoon. It's called a scoop.	Like an ice-cream scoop!
	What do you think we will be using it for in science?	To scoop things up.
Funnel	Have you seen this before?	My mom uses that for the car.
	It's called a funnel. Where else have you seen this?	In the kitchen. My uncle uses it sometimes to pour things.
	Can you describe it?	It's round on the ends. It's bigger on one end, and it's hollow.
Beaker	Have you seen this before?	We used it for science last year to measure and pour water.
	It's called a beaker. Where else have you seen this?	
Vial	This is a vial. What do you think we will be using it for in science?	To hold small things.

A kit inventory script from the Solids and Liquids Module

Comprehensible Input

In order to initiate their own sense-making process, students must be able to access the information presented to them. We refer to this ability as comprehensible input. Students must understand the essence of new ideas and concepts before beginning the process of constructing new scientific meaning. The strategies for comprehensible input used in FOSS ensure that the delivery of instruction is understandable while providing students with the opportunity to grapple with new ideas and the critically important relationships between concepts. Additional linguistic accommodations such as repetition, visual aids, emphasis on procedural vocabulary, and auditory reinforcement can also be used to convey meaning of key concepts to ELs. (See Table 1. Linguistic supports for kindergarten through second grade organized by proficiency levels.)

Content objectives. The focus question for each investigation part frames the activity objectives—what students should know or be able to do at the end of the part. Together the focus questions help students build a conceptual framework for understanding the overarching anchor phenomenon explored in the module. Making the learning objectives or targets clear and explicit helps English learners prepare to process the delivery of new information, and helps you maintain the focus of the investigation. Write the focus question on the board and read it aloud. At the end of the investigation part, ask students to write or glue in the focus question and write or dictate the response. During the Wrap-Up/Warm-Up you can check their responses for understanding.

Multiple exposures. Repeat the activity as a class, at a center during independent work time, or in an analogous but slightly different context, ideally one that incorporates elements that are culturally relevant to students.

Visual aids. On the board or chart paper, write out and illustrate the steps for conducting the investigation. This will provide a visual reference. Use graphic representations (illustrations drawn and labeled in front of students) to review the concepts explored in the active investigations. In addition to the concrete objects included in the kit, use realia to augment the activity to help English learners build understanding and make cultural connections. Simple graphic organizers (webs, Venn diagrams, T-tables, flowcharts, etc.) aid comprehension by helping students see how ideas (concepts) are related.

Strategies for Comprehensible Input
- *Content objectives*
- *Multiple exposures*
- *Visual aids*
- *Supported reading*
- *Procedural vocabulary*

▶ **ELPS NOTE**
These strategies support the ELPS 8–10 and WIDA Standard 4.

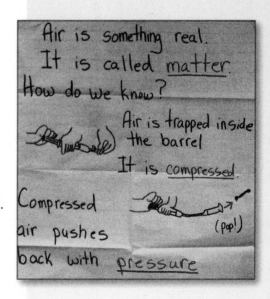

Air is something real. It is called <u>matter</u>. How do we know?

Air is trapped inside the barrel

It is <u>compressed</u>.

Compressed air pushes back with <u>pressure</u>

(pop!)

Procedural Vocabulary

Add	Illustrate
Analyze	Immerse
Assemble	Investigate
Attach	Label
Calculate	List
Change	Measure
Classify	Mix
Collect	Observe
Communicate	Open
Compare	Order
Connect	Organize
Construct	Pour
Contrast	Predict
Describe	Prepare
Demonstrate	Record
Determine	Represent
Draw	Scratch
Evaluate	Separate
Examine	Sort
Explain	Stir
Explore	Subtract
Fill	Summarize
Graph	Test
Identify	Weigh

▶ **ELPS NOTE**

These strategies support the
ELPS 8–10 and WIDA Standard 4.

Supported reading. In addition to the reading comprehension strategies suggested in the Reading Strand section of this chapter, English learners can also benefit from methods such as front-loading key words, phrases, and complex text structures before reading or using preview-review (main ideas are previewed in the primary language, read in English, and reviewed in the primary language).

Procedural vocabulary. Make sure students understand the meaning of the words used in the directions describing what they should be doing during the investigation. These may or may not be science-specific words. Use techniques such as modeling, demonstrating, and body language (gestures) to explain procedural meaning in the context of the investigation. The words students will encounter in FOSS include those listed in the sidebar. To build academic literacy, English learners need to learn the multiple meanings of these words and their specific meanings in the context of science.

Developing Academic Language

As students learn the nuances of the English language, it is critical that they build proficiency in academic language in order to participate fully in the cognitive demands of school. Academic language refers to the more abstract, complex, and specific aspects of language, such as the words, grammatical structure, and discourse markers that are needed for higher cognitive learning. FOSS investigations introduce and provide opportunities for students to practice using the academic vocabulary needed to access and meaningfully engage with science ideas.

Science language learning objectives. Consider the English proficiency levels of your ELs and incorporate specific language-development objectives that will support their engagement in the science and engineering practices. You might focus on a specific word knowledge skill (a way to expand use of vocabulary by looking at root words, prefixes, and suffixes), a linguistic pattern or structure for oral discussion and writing, or a reading-comprehension strategy. Recording in students' science notebooks is a productive place to optimize science learning and language objectives.

To help students meet the language demands of practices like constructing explanations and engaging in argument from evidence, first, consider the analytical or cognitive tasks required to meet the language objective. For example, to engage in argument from evidence, students will need to be able to do these things.

- Distinguish between a claim and supporting evidence or explanation.

- Analyze whether expressed evidence supports, contradicts, or is irrelevant to a claim.

- Analyze how well a model (explanation) and evidence are aligned.

- Construct an argument.

To accomplish these analytical tasks, students will use both receptive and productive language functions.

The receptive language functions are what students do in order to *comprehend* others' written and oral arguments. They include identifying, distinguishing, comparing, evaluating, and reflecting on the words and their meaning, and synthesizing them into a concept.

The productive language functions are how students communicate their claims, evidence, and reasoning in support of and against the arguments of others. This includes structuring and ordering written or verbal reasoning for a position; selecting and presenting key evidence and reasoning to support or refute claims; questioning or critiquing arguments of others; suggesting alternative reasoning; refining one's own thinking; and negotiating differing conclusions.

Here's an example from the **Pebbles, Sand, and Silt Module** (grade 2). Students discuss whether soil changes or not. The content objective is for students to deepen their understanding of where soil comes from. They engage in argument by <u>identifying</u> arguments that are supported by evidence and <u>listening actively</u> to arguments to indicate agreement or disagreement. Students are tasked with providing evidence for and against the claim, "Soil does not change." The cognitive task for students is to <u>analyze</u> whether evidence supports or contradicts a claim. What are the language functions required for this task?

- ***Receptive language function.*** Students need to understand the concepts of weathering and decay. They need to comprehend the evidence presented by others and determine its relevancy. They must identify the connection (Is there evidence to support the claim?), compare it to their own ideas (Does this connection make sense to me?).

- **Productive language functions.** Students need to communicate their evidence orally and describe why they think it supports or refutes the claim. They might also ask questions, request further explanations, and refine or change their own thinking.

  So students must tackle not just the content of weathering and decay, but also the skills of listening and communicating their reasoning. Identifying those skills allows for better differentiation during instruction.

Crafting a Language Objective. A science language objective takes into account both science content and language goals. When planning for ELD and science, pay particular attention to the analytical tasks and the corresponding language functions. Consider these questions.

1. What are the science concepts (disciplinary core ideas) students will learn?

2. How will students engage in a practice(s) to deepen their conceptual understanding?

3. How will students process and communicate what they are thinking, given their level of English proficiency?

Here is a language objective based on these questions using the "What is soil?" example.

Students will

- Present evidence for and against a claim,

- Communicate whether they agree or disagree or add on to the ideas of others

Differentiation. In this example, to address the varying levels of students' English proficiency, you, the teacher, might break down the language objective into three levels of expectation—emerging, expanding, and bridging.

1. **Emerging.** State evidence that supports or refutes the claim using sentence frames [e.g., "Soil (changes, does not change) because _____ ."] as well as open responses.

2. **Expanding.** State evidence that supports the claim and provides reasoning, using an expanding set of learned phrases (e.g., "I think _____ ." "My evidence for _____ is _____ .") as well as open responses.

3. **Bridging**. State evidence that supports the claim and provides reasoning, using a variety of learned phrases (e.g., "I think _____ . My evidence for is _____ ." My evidence against

is _____ .") as well as open responses and provide counter arguments and elaborate on the ideas of others (e.g., "I agree with _____ because _____ ." "I disagree with _____ because _____ ." "I would like to add that _____ .")

Strategies Toolkit. The next phase is to think about scaffolds to make sure all students participate. For this example, the "Put yourself on the line," strategy is appropriate. Students form a single line (a continuum) with those that agree strongly that soil changes at one end, those who agree strongly that soil does not change at the other end, and those who are open to both ideas or not quite sure, in the middle of the line. Students discuss their reasoning with neighbors and decide where they should position themselves on the continuum.

Here are additional routines and structures that specifically support emergent bilingual students in producing the complex oral language needed for argumentation. (These are modified from Zwiers et al. 2014.)

- Pair students up based on their opposing claims. Student A shares his or her thinking while student B listens. Student B responds by paraphrasing what A said and then asking a question that helps the other think more deeply about their idea. *Why do you think that? What is your evidence?*

- Give students time to get their ducks in a row by first discussing their arguments with one another before the whole–class discussion.

- Provide sentence frames that will encourage active listening and productive talk.

  - I agree/disagree with _____ because _____ .

  - I have another idea _____ .

  - I am wondering what would happen if _____ .

  - Why do you think _____ ?

  - Would it matter if _____ ?

- Have students write/draw their ideas before presenting them. (Speaking before writing also gives students the opportunity to practice using and hearing complex language in preparation for writing.)

Soil does not change.

Strongly agree

Strongly disagree

Activity description adapted from Gould, D 2014. Science Scope. Let's Talk Science: Seeding Argumentation About Cells and Growth, pp. 65–75.

Providing Oral Practice
- *Pair and small-group discussions*
- *Science talk*
- *Oral presentations*
- *Poems, chants, and songs*
- *Teacher feedback*

Providing Oral Practice

Students acquire English when they have lots of opportunities to hear and practice using the language in meaningful ways. Make sure to allow sufficient time for student discussions and use the protocols and strategies described in the Speaking and Listening Strand section. FOSS investigations are designed for student engagement in collaborative discussions as described in the CCELA CCSS.ELA for all students and are especially critical for students developing their proficiency in English.

Establishing a culture of talk. Establishing and maintaining a culture of talk in the classroom where the voices of all students are respected and valued is key to fostering robust and equitable academic discourse. This means allowing flaws to surface in student's models, procedures, designs, and explanations as well as limitations in their English-language proficiency. The classroom culture should convey a spirit of shared thinking and discovery in which all students feel encouraged to ask each other questions, push for further explanations, and refute the claims of others. Constructing explanations and engaging in argument from evidence provides emergent bilingual students with the opportunity to hear examples of the type of discourse they are expected to produce (Quinn, Lee, and Valdés, 2012).

Pair and small-group discussions. As a rule, instead of launching questions to the whole group for one student to answer, use think-pair-share, turn and talk, or elbow partner conversations so every student has a chance to share his/her ideas aloud. These strategies not only provide more air time for students to practice English, but also increase the engagement level for everyone. When organizing students for small group work, consider the English proficiency levels of students and mix them up so there is at least one student who is a native speaker or at high level of English proficiency in each group. Use scaffolds such as "put your two cents in" or sentence frames on cards or placemats to support language production.

Science talk. While not all students will participate verbally in whole group science talks at all times, listening to others make claims, provide evidence, and build on the ideas of others provides ELs with examples of how the language sounds and the structures and vocabulary used to communicate ideas in science and engineering.

TEACHING NOTE

Science talk is any whole-group discussion that takes place during science. A sense-making discussion is a specific science talk meant to extract meaning from data.

Oral presentations. Use linguistic supports for students according to their level of proficiency for presenting information orally. For example, allow for thinking time, simple sentences, and flawed language for beginners. Provide models and explicit expectations for the type of language students should use in their presentations.

Poems, chants, and songs. Vocabulary words and phrases can be reinforced using content-rich poems, raps, chants, and songs after students have been introduced to the concepts. As a whole-group activity, create songs, poems, and chants that incorporate what students have learned. When using other resources, make sure the science content is accurate.

Teacher feedback. Rephrase or recast students' incomplete or flawed statements or questions, So what you're saying is…? You're question then is …? The word you're looking for is ….

Vocabulary development. The Science-Vocabulary Development section in this chapter describes the ways in which science vocabulary is introduced and developed in the context of an active investigation and suggests methods and strategies that can be used to support vocabulary development during instruction in English language arts and ELD. In addition to science vocabulary, students also need to learn the nonspecific-content words that facilitate deeper understanding and communication skills. Words such as compare, identify, direct, produce, receive, source, and reflect are words used in the investigations and FOSS Science Resources and are frequently used in other content areas. Learning these academic vocabulary words gives students a more precise and complex way of practicing and communicating productive thinking. Consider using the strategies described in the Science-Vocabulary Development section to explicitly teach targeted, high-leverage words that can be used in multiple ways and that can help students make connections to other words and concepts. Sentence frames, word wall, concept maps, and cognitive content dictionary are strategies that have been found to be effective with academic-vocabulary development.

Table 1. FOSS and WIDA /ELPS Integration Chart

FOSS Instructional Design	Interactive/Collaborative Modality
Setting the Context: **SEPs: Asking questions and defining problems;** **Planning investigations** • Introduce phenomena • Activate prior knowledge • Present the focus question • Challenge • Make predictions	**ELPS 2.** Participate in oral and written exchanges of information and ideas, and respond to peer or audience comments and questions.
Active Investigation: **SEPs: Carrying out investigations** • Collaborative groups • Following directions • Making observations and measurements • Testing and evaluating	**ELPS 2.** Participate in oral and written exchanges of information and ideas, and respond to peer comments and questions.
Data management: **SEPs: Analyzing and interpreting data; Using mathematics and computational thinking;** • Record in notebook • Organize and process data • Make claims based on evidence	**ELPS 2.** Participate in oral and written exchanges of information and ideas and responding to peer comments and questions.

Receptive Modality	Productive Modality
ELPS 1. Construct meaning from oral presentations through listening, reading, and viewing **ELPS 2.** Determine the meaning of words and phrases in oral presentations. **WIDA.** Process rich descriptive discourse with complex sentences, cohesive and organized, related ideas.	**ELPS 3.** Speak and write about complex informational topics. **ELPS 4.** Construct oral and written claims and support them with reasoning and evidence. **ELPS 7.** Adapt language choices to purpose, task, and audience when speaking and writing. **WIDA.** Produce a variety of complex grammatical structures matched to purpose and a broad range of sentence patterns characteristic of science.
ELPS 2. Determine the meaning of words and phrases in oral presentations and and informational text. **WIDA.** Process rich descriptive discourse with complex sentences, cohesive and organized, related ideas.	**ELPS 3.** Speak and write about complex informational topics. **ELPS 7.** Adapt language choices to purpose, task, and audience when speaking and writing. **WIDA.** Produce technical and abstract science language, including content-specific collocations, and words and expressions with precise meaning
WIDA. Process rich descriptive discourse with complex sentences, cohesive and organized, related ideas.	**ELPS 3.** Speak and write about complex informational topics. **ELPS 4.** Construct oral and written claims and support them with reasoning and evidence. **ELPS 7.** Adapt language choices to purpose, task, and audience when speaking and writing. **WIDA.** Produce technical and abstract science language, including content-specific collocations, and words and expressions with precise meaning

Table 1. FOSS and WIDA /ELPS Integration Chart (continued)

FOSS Instructional Design	Interactive/Collaborative Modality
Analysis: **SEPs: Analyzing and interpreting data; Developing and using models; Constructing explanations; Engaging in Argument from evidence** • Sense-making discussions • Writing in notebooks • Vocabulary development • Answer the focus questions • Wrap-up/Warm-up review of concepts learned	**ELPS 2.** Participate in oral and written exchanges of information, ideas, and analyses, responding to peer, audience, or reader comments and questions. **ELPS 5.** Conduct research and evaluate and communicate findings to answer questions or solve problems. **ELPS 6.** Analyze and critique the arguments of others orally and in writing
Reading **SEPs: Obtaining, evaluating, and communicating information** • Before, during and after reading strategies • Active Reading • Making notes • Sense-making Discussions • Answer thinking questions **Multimedia activities**	**ELPS 2.** Participate in oral and written exchanges of information, ideas, and analyses, responding to peer, audience, or reader comments and questions. **ELPS 5.** Conduct research and evaluate and communicate findings to answer questions or solve problems. **ELPS 6.** Analyze and critique the arguments of others orally and in writing
Assessment **SEPs: Analyzing and interpreting data; Developing and using models; Constructing explanations; Engaging in Argument from evidence; Obtaining, evaluating, and communicating information** • Writing in notebooks • Response Sheets • I-Checks/Surveys • Next Step Strategies • Performance Assessments	**ELPS 2.** Participate in oral and written exchanges of information, ideas, and analyses, responding to peer, audience, or reader comments and questions. **ELPS 5.** Conduct research and evaluate and communicate findings to answer questions or solve problems. **ELPS 6.** Analyze and critique the arguments of others orally and in writing

Interpretive/Receptive Modality	Productive Modality
ELPS 1. Construct meaning from oral presentations through listening, reading, and viewing. **ELPS 8.** Determine the meaning of words and phrases in oral presentations and informational text. **WIDA.** Process technical and abstract science language, words and expressions with shades of meaning.	**ELPS 3.** Speak and write about complex informational topics. **ELPS 4.** Construct oral and written claims and support them with reasoning and evidence. **ELPS 7.** Adapt language choices to purpose, task, and audience when speaking and writing. **WIDA.** Produce multiple, complex sentences and organized, cohesive, and coherent expression of ideas characteristic of science.
ELPS 1. Construct meaning from informational text through listening, reading, and viewing **ELPS 8.** Determine the meaning of words and phrases in informational text. **WIDA.** Process a variety of complex grammatical structures and sentence patterns characteristic of science. **WIDA.** Process technical and abstract science language, and words and expressions with shades of meaning.	**ELPS 3.** Speak and write about complex informational texts and topics. **ELPS 4.** Construct oral and written claims and support them with reasoning and evidence. **WIDA.** Produce multiple, complex sentences and organized, cohesive, and coherent expression of ideas characteristic of science.
ELPS 1. Construct meaning from oral presentations and informational text through listening, reading, and viewing **ELPS 8.** Determine the meaning of words and phrases in oral presentations and informational text. **WIDA.** Process technical and abstract science language, and words and expressions with shades of meaning.	**ELPS 3.** Speak and write about complex informational texts and topics. **ELPS 4.** Construct oral and written claims and support them with reasoning and evidence. **WIDA.** Produce technical and abstract science language, including content-specific collocations, and words and expressions with precise meaning

Table 2. Linguistic supports for Grades K–2

	Levels 1-2. Entering and Emerging	Level 3. Developing
Listening	• Use visuals, slower speech, verbal cues, and gestures. • Highlight important vocabulary words. • Monitor for student understanding.	• Use levels 1-2 supports when introducing new concepts. • Repeat/rephrase instructions and information when necessary. • Ask students to repeat or paraphrase what they heard.
Speaking	• Allow for one-word or short-phrase answers. • Provide simple sentence frames and word walls. • Model pronunciation and use of vocabulary words in context.	• Allow for thinking time, simple sentence responses, and use of present tense. • Provide sentence frames and interactive word walls. • Model and have students practice pronunciation and accurate use of vocabulary words and sentence structures to convey science ideas.
Reading	• Read *FOSS Science Resources* aloud in short chunks. Use visual supports such as illustrations, gestures, pantomime, and objects. • Use careful enunciation and slower speech. • Point out science words on the word wall, charts, and other classroom print.	• Discuss predictable text structures, reference the active investigation, review new vocabulary words, and use visual and linguistic supports during read-alouds. • Practice reading science word walls and charts.
Writing	• Allow emergent forms of writing (pictures, letter-like forms, mock words, scribbling). • Model shared notebook-writing activities. • Provide opportunities to use new vocabulary words, phrases, or short sentences that have been introduced in the active investigation. • Explicitly teach English print conventions.	• Ask students to explain their thinking orally before writing or drawing. • Support participation in shared notebook-writing activities. • Provide opportunities to express ideas in short sentences using new vocabulary words used in class discussions. • Allow for use of primary-language words, spelling patterns, word order, and literal translations.

Level 4. Expanding	Level 5. Bridging
• Provide processing time and supports from lower levels when needed. • Encourage students to request clarification, repetition, and rephrasing.	• Provide processing time when necessary. • Use supports from lower levels for complex ideas and new science vocabulary and language structures.
• Allow for pauses to restate, repeat, or search for words and phrases to clarify meaning. • Provide time for speaking in pairs before whole class discussions.	• Give support with low-frequency or academically demanding vocabulary when necessary. • Introduce higher-level language functions and structures.
• Provide visual and linguistic support when needed to gain or confirm meaning while reading aloud. • Provide support when decoding *FOSS Science Resources* articles.	• Provide support when needed for comprehension of main points and supporting ideas while reading aloud. • Provide support when needed when decoding and understanding *FOSS Science Resources* articles.
• Ask students to describe and explain their ideas in their notebooks with details. • Support participation in shared notebook-writing activities.	• Ask students to describe and explain their ideas in their notebooks with a higher level of complexity and detail. • Encourage full participation in shared notebook-writing activities.

REFERENCES

Applebee, A. 1984. "Writing and Reasoning." *Review of Educational Research* 54 (winter): 577–596.

Bereiter, C. 2002. *Education and Mind in the Knowledge Age.* Hillsdale, NJ: Erlbaum.

Black Hills Special Services Cooperative. 2006. "3-2-1 Strategy." In *On Target: More Strategies to Guide Learning.* Rapid City, SD. http://www.sdesa6.org/content/resources.htm.

Dyasi, H. M. 2006. "Visions of Inquiry: Science." In *Linking Science and Literacy in the K–8 Classroom*, ed. R. Douglas, K. Worth, and W. Binder. Arlington, VA: NSTA Press.

Gibbons, P. 2002. *Scaffolding Language, Scaffolding Learning.* Portsmouth, NH: Heinemann.

Graham, S., and M. Herbert. 2010. *Writing to Read: Evidence for How Writing Can Improve Reading.* New York: Carnegie.

Hamilton, G. 2002. *Content-Area Reading Strategies: Science.* Portland, ME: Walch Publishing.

Hand, B., and V. Prain. 2002. "Teachers Implementing Writing-to-Learn Strategies in Junior Secondary Science: A Case Study." *Science Education* 86: 737–755.

Harvey, S. 1998. *Nonfiction Matters: Reading, Writing, and Research in Grades 3–8.* Portland, ME: Stenhouse.

Harvey, S., and A. Goudvis. 2007. *Strategies That Work: Teaching Comprehension for Understanding and Engagement.* Portland, ME: Stenhouse.

Keene, E., and S. Zimmermann. 2007. *Mosaic of Thought: The Power of Comprehension Strategies.* 2nd ed. Portsmouth, NH: Heinemann.

Keys, C. 1999. *Revitalizing Instruction in Scientific Genres: Connecting Knowledge Production with Writing to Learn in Science.* Athens: University of Georgia.

Lieberman, G. A., and L.L. Hoody. 1998. *Closing the Achievement Gap: Using the Environment as an Integrating Context for Learning.* San Diego, CA: State Education and Environment Roundtable.

National Research Council. 2010. *A Framework for K–12 Science Education: Practices, Crosscutting Concepts, and Core Ideas.* Committee on Conceptual Framework for New Science Education Standards.

Ostlund, K. 1998. "What the Research Says about Science Process Skills: How Can Teaching Science Process Skills Improve Student Performance in Reading, Language Arts, and Mathematics?" *Electronic Journal of Science Education* 2 (4).

Wellington, J., and J. Osborne. 2001. *Language and Literacy in Science Education.* Buckingham, UK: Open University Press.

Winokur, J., and K. Worth. 2006. "Talk in the Science Classroom: Looking at What Students and Teachers Need to Know and Be Able to Do." In *Linking Science and Literacy in the K–8 Classroom*, ed. R. Douglas, K. Worth, and W. Binder. Arlington, VA: NSTA Press.

Zwiers, J., S. O'Hara, and R. Pritchard. 2014. *Common Core Standards in Diverse Classrooms: Essential Practices for Developing Academic Language and Disciplinary Literacy.* Portland, ME: Stenhouse.

FOSS and Common Core ELA – Grade 2

FOSS and Common Core ELA — Grade 2

Contents

INTRODUCTION

Each FOSS investigation follows a similar design to provide multiple exposures to science concepts. The design includes these pedagogies.

- Active investigation, including outdoor experiences

- Writing in science notebooks to answer focus questions

- Reading in *FOSS Science Resources*

- Assessment to monitor progress and motivate student reflection on learning

In practice, these components are seamlessly integrated into a continuum designed to maximize every student's opportunity to learn. An instructional sequence may move from one pedagogy to another and back again to ensure adequate coverage of a concept.

The FOSS instructional design recognizes the important role of language in science learning. Throughout the pedagogical design elements, students engage in the practices of the Common Core State Standards (CCSS) for English Language Arts (ELA). The purpose of this chapter is to provide the big picture of how FOSS provides opportunities for the development and exercising of these practices through science. On the following pages, there is a chart that identifies the opportunities for second grade and where the relevant opportunities are found within the three FOSS modules.

Guiding Principles

When integrating language-arts instruction with FOSS, keep in mind these guiding principles:

- FOSS investigations follow a clear and coherent conceptual flow and a consistent instructional design. Students develop science knowledge by building a framework of concepts and supporting ideas.

- Common Core State Standards for ELA are introduced, developed, and practiced in the context of learning science content and engaging in the science and engineering practices. Students read and comprehend complex science texts related to their prior experience and knowledge. They write informational/explanatory texts, arguments to support claims, and narratives about experience in science. They engage in collaborative discussions about science and learn new vocabulary and language structures in context.

- The decision to use additional science texts, writing tasks, oral discourse opportunities, and vocabulary development activities is based on how well they address the science as well as the ELA standards.

- Instruction is differentiated to meet the needs of all students; the linguistic accommodations that are made for English learners support comprehensible input and accelerate academic language development. Language objectives for English learners in science instruction include the application of strategies that support construction of meaning from academic discussions and complex text, participation in productive discourse, and the ability to express ideas in writing clearly and coherently according to task, purpose, and audience.

- Formative assessment tools are used routinely to measure progress toward science understanding, use of science and engineering practices, and meeting literacy and language development goals. Assessment is viewed as a way to make student thinking visible and to determine next steps for instruction for both science and literacy. Instruction includes opportunities for students to assess themselves and peers.

Second grade is an exciting year as students increase independence in making meaning from texts read aloud and on their own. Their vocabularies increase and they are continuing to develop their communication skills. Second graders are expected to use the science and engineering practices to demonstrate their understanding of the

---

TEACHING NOTE

Adhering to these guiding principles optimizes instructional time and, most importantly, benefits student learning by providing authentic and relevant contexts for building content knowledge, applying meaning-making strategies, and developing language and literacy skills.

Introduction

core ideas. To accomplish this, students learn to find patterns and evidence in texts, describe how images support ideas, use text features to locate information, and communicate their ideas orally and in written form using models, drawings, and writing.

Instructional Flow

In almost all investigations, the instructional flow is the same and provides these opportunities for effective integration of ELA standards.

- When **setting the context** for the lesson, students activate prior knowledge through class or small-group discussions where they ask and answer questions to clarify comprehension, gather additional information, and deepen understanding (SL 3), or recount information. (SL 4).

- During the **active investigation**, students are expected to work with partners and in collaborative groups, and to engage in teacher-led discussions where they build on each other's ideas and ask for clarification and further explanation as needed. (SL 1).

- In the **data management** phase, students make observations, record, and organize data in their notebooks. (W 7) The notebook provides a space for students to recall information from experiences and to gather information to answer the focus question. (W 8) and to use words and phrases acquired through conversations and readings. (L 6).

- The **analysis** phase involves discussing data, constructing and writing explanations, and engaging in argumentation. Here students are making meaning by writing explanatory texts (W 2), writing opinion pieces supporting a point of view with reasons. (W 1), or participating in a shared research or writing project. (W 7).

- **Reading** articles in *FOSS Science Resources* and other recommended readings provides a plethora of opportunities to address all the third-grade reading standards for informational text.

- Lastly, the **assessment** tools and next-Step strategies for engaging students in high-level critical thinking support the development of the CCSS capacities of the literate individual: demonstrate independence, build strong content knowledge, comprehend as well as critique, and value evidence.

Again, we have provided you with some examples of how FOSS connects to the second-grade ELA standards; there are many more opportunities waiting to be created and explored by you and your students.

TEACHING NOTE

Throughout the second-grade FOSS modules, opportunities for addressing the ELA standards have been noted; however, these examples should not be considered the only places for integrating literacy skills.

FOSS and Common Core ELA — Grade 2

READING STANDARDS FOR INFORMATIONAL TEXT

Standard	Solids and Liquids Module
Key Ideas and Details	
1. Ask and answer such questions as *who*, *what*, *where*, *when*, *why*, and *how* to demonstrate understanding of key details in a text.	Discuss articles in *FOSS Science Resources* Inv 1, Part 1, Step 18; Inv 1, Part 2, Step 15; Inv 1, Part 4, Step 18; Inv 2, Part 3, Step 18 Inv 3, Part 4, Step 9; Inv 3, Part 5, Step 12 Inv 4, Part 2, Step 16; Inv 4, Part 4, Steps 21, 23
2. Identify the main topic of a multiparagraph text as well as the focus of specific paragraphs within the text.	Discuss and review articles in *FOSS Science Resources* Inv 3, Part 4, Steps 8-9; Inv 3, Part 5, Step 12 Inv 4, Part 2, Step 16; Inv 4, Part 4, Steps 20-21
3. Describe the connection between a series of historical events, scientific ideas or concepts, or Steps in technical procedures in a text.	Discuss articles in *FOSS Science Resources* Inv 2, Part 3, Step 17; Inv 3, Part 4, Steps 8-9 Inv 4, Part 2, Step 15; Inv 4, Part 4, Steps 17, 23
Craft and Structure	
4. Determine the meaning of words and phrases in a text relevant to a *grade 2 topic or subject area*.	All investigations provide opportunities for students to determine the meaning of new words and phrases while reading articles in *FOSS Science Resources*. Selected examples Inv 1, Part 4, Steps 2, 17; Inv 4, Part 2, Step 15
5. Know and use various text features (e.g., captions, bold print, subheadings, glossaries, indexes, electronic menus, icons) to locate key facts or information in a text efficiently.	Read and discuss articles in *FOSS Science Resources* Inv 1, Part 1, Step 17; Inv 4, Part 2, Step 16
6. Identify the main purpose of a text, including what the author wants to answer, explain, or describe.	Read and discuss articles in *FOSS Science Resources* Inv 1, Part 1, Step 17; Inv 1, Part 2, Step 15 Inv 2, Part 3, Step 17; Inv 3, Part 4, Step 9 Inv 4, Part 2, Step 16; Inv 4, Part 4, Step 20

Common Core State Standards for English Language Arts and Literacy in History/Social Studies Science and Technical Subjects (National Governors Association Center for Best Practices and Council of Chief State School Officers, 2010).

Insects and Plants Module	Pebbles, Sand, and Silt Module
Discuss articles in *FOSS Science Resources* Inv 2, Part 3, Steps 10-12; Inv 2, Part 4, Steps 19, 20 Inv 3, Part 2, Step 21 Inv 4, Part 2, Step 20; Inv 4, Part 3, Steps 10-11 Inv 5, Part 3, Steps 16-17	Discuss articles in *FOSS Science Resources* Inv 1, Part 4, Step 16; Inv 1, Part 5, Step 6 Inv 2, Part 4, Step 30 Inv 3, Part 1, Step 12; Inv 3, Part 5, Step 12 Inv 4, Part 2, Steps 7-9, 24; Inv 4, Part 3, Steps 3, 8; Inv 4, Part 4, Steps 1, 3, 5
Discuss and review articles in *FOSS Science Resources* Inv 1, Part 1, Step 19; Inv 2, Part 3, Step 9; Inv 2, Part 4, Step 18; Inv 3, Part 2, Step 20; Inv 4, Part 2, Step 19; Inv 4, Part 3, Step 9; Inv 5, Part 3, Step 15	Discuss and review articles in *FOSS Science Resources* Inv 1, Part 4, Step 15-16; Inv 2, Part 2, Steps 8-9; Inv 2, Part 4, Steps 22, 30; Inv 4, Part 2, Steps 8-9; Inv 4, Part 3, Step 5; Inv 4, Part 4, Step 5
Discuss articles in *FOSS Science Resources* Inv 2, Part 3, Steps 9-10; Inv 4, Part 2, Step 20	Discuss articles in *FOSS Science Resources* Inv 2, Part 4, Steps 22, 30; Inv 3, Part 1, Step 11; Inv 3, Part 5, Step 13; Inv 4, Part 2, Step 8; Inv 4, Part 4, Steps 1, 3
All investigations provide opportunities for students to determine the meaning of new words and phrases while reading articles in *FOSS Science Resources*. Selected examples Inv 2, Part 4, Step 18; Inv 5, Part 3, Step 14	All investigations provide opportunities for students to determine the meaning of new words and phrases while reading articles in *FOSS Science Resources*. Selected examples Inv 1, Part 4, Step 15; Inv 1, Part 5, Step 6; Inv 2, Part 2, Step 8; Inv 3, Part 5, Step 12; Inv 4, Part 3, Steps 2-3
Read and discuss articles in *FOSS Science Resources* Inv 1, Part 1, Step 18; Inv 2, Part 4, Steps 18-20 Inv 5, Part 3, Steps 16-17	Read and discuss articles in *FOSS Science Resources* Inv 1, Part 4, Step 15; Inv 2, Part 2, Step 8 Inv 3, Part 5, Step 12 Inv 4, Part 2, Step 8; Inv 4, Part 4, Steps 1, 5
Read and discuss articles in *FOSS Science Resources* Inv 1, Part 1, Step 19; Inv 2, Part 4, Step 20 Inv 5, Part 3, Steps 15-17	Read and discuss articles in *FOSS Science Resources* Inv 1, Part 4, Steps 15-16; Inv 2, Part 2, Step 8 Inv 4, Part 2, Steps 7-9; Inv 4, Part 2, Steps 24-25

READING STANDARDS FOR INFORMATIONAL TEXT (continued)

Standard	Solids and Liquids Module
Integration of Knowledge and Ideas	
7. Explain how specific images (e.g., a diagram showing how a machine works) contribute to and clarify a text.	All investigations provide opportunities for students to explain how the photographs and diagrams help them understand the articles in *FOSS Science Resources*. Selected examples Inv 1, Part 1, Step 18; Inv 2, Part 3, Step 17 Inv 3, Part 5, Step 12; Inv 4, Part 2, Step 16
8. Describe how reasons support specific points the author makes in a text.	Read and discuss articles in *FOSS Science Resources* Inv 1, Part 2, Step 15; Inv 2, Part 3, Step 17 Inv 4, Part 2, Step 16
9. Compare and contrast the most important points presented by two texts on the same topic.	Students can read *FOSS Science Resources* as well as readings suggested on FOSSweb. Using these two texts allows students to compare and contrast important science ideas. Selected examples Inv 3, Part 5, Step 11 Inv 4, Language Extension. Describe oobleck
Range of Reading and Level of Text Complexity	
10. By the end of year, read and comprehend informational texts, including history/social studies, science, and technical texts, in the grades 2–3 text complexity band proficiently, with scaffolding as needed at the high end of the range.	All investigations provide opportunities for students to develop their ability to read and comprehend complex informational science text such as *FOSS Science Resources*.

Insects and Plants Module	Pebbles, Sand, and Silt Module
All investigations provide opportunities for students to explain how the photographs and diagrams help them understand the articles in *FOSS Science Resources*. Selected examples Inv 2, Part 3, Step 10; Inv 4, Part 3, Steps 9-10 Inv 5, Part 3, Step 15	All investigations provide opportunities for students to explain how the photographs and diagrams help them understand the articles in *FOSS Science Resources*. Selected examples Inv 1, Part 4, Steps 15-16; Inv 1, Part 5, Steps 5-6 Inv 2, Part 2, Step 8; Inv 2, Part 4, Step 29 Inv 3, Part 1, Steps 11-12; Inv 4, Part 2, Step 7
Read and discuss articles in *FOSS Science Resources* Inv 2, Part 4, Steps 18-19	Read and discuss articles in *FOSS Science Resources* Inv 1, Part 4, Step 16; Inv 2, Part 2, Steps 8-9 Inv 3, Part 1, Steps 11-12; Inv 4, Part 2, Steps 7-8
Students can read *FOSS Science Resources* as well as readings suggested on FOSSweb. Using these two texts, allows students to compare and contrast important science ideas. Selected examples Inv 1, Language extension. Read *Lifetimes* Inv 4, Part 2, Step 20	Students can read *FOSS Science Resources* as well as readings suggested on FOSSweb. Using these two texts, allows students to compare and contrast important science ideas. Selected examples Inv 1, Part 4, Steps 1, 16; Inv 1. Language extension. Make stone soup; Inv 1. Language extension. Read about special rocks; Inv 4, Part 4, Step 5
All investigations provide opportunities for students to develop their ability to read and comprehend complex informational science text such as *FOSS Science Resources*.	All investigations provide opportunities for students to develop their ability to read and comprehend complex informational science text such as *FOSS Science Resources*.

READING STANDARDS: FOUNDATIONAL SKILLS

Standard	Solids and Liquids Module
Phonics and Word Recognition 3. Know and apply grade-level phonics and word analysis skills in decoding words. a. Distinguish long and short vowels when reading regularly spelled one-syllable words. b. Know spelling-sound correspondences for additional common vowel teams. c. Decode regularly spelled two-syllable words with long vowels. d. Decode words with common prefixes and suffixes. e. Identify words with inconsistent but common spelling-sound correspondences. f. Recognize and read grade-appropriate irregularly spelled words.	All investigations provide opportunities for students to apply phonics and word analysis skills in decoding words while reading articles in *FOSS Science Resources*. Selected example Inv 4, Part 4, Step 20
Fluency 4. Read with sufficient accuracy and fluency to support comprehension. a. Read grade-level text with purpose and understanding. b. Read grade-level text orally with accuracy, appropriate rate, and expression on successive readings. c. Use context to confirm or self-correct word recognition and understanding, rereading as necessary.	All investigations provide opportunities for students to practice reading with accuracy and fluency. Selected examples Inv 1, Part 1, Step 17 Inv 2, Part 3, Step 17 Inv 4, Part 4, Step 20

Insects and Plants Module	Pebbles, Sand, and Silt Module
All investigations provide opportunities for students to apply phonics and word analysis skills in decoding words while reading articles in *FOSS Science Resources*. Selected example Inv 5, Part 3, Steps 15-16	All investigations provide opportunities for students to apply phonics and word analysis skills in decoding words while reading articles in *FOSS Science Resources*. Selected example Inv 2, Part 4, Step 21
All investigations provide opportunities for students to practice reading with accuracy and fluency. Selected examples Inv 2, Part 3, Step 9; Inv 2, Part 4, Step 18 Inv 3, Part 2, Steps 19-20 Inv 4, Part 2, Step 19; Inv 4, Part 3, Step 9 Inv 5, Part 3, Steps 15-17	All investigations provide opportunities for students to practice reading with accuracy and fluency. Selected examples Inv 1, Part 4, Step 15 Inv 2, Part 2, Step 8; Inv 2, Part 4, Steps 21, 29 Inv 3, Part 1, Step 11; Inv 3, Part 5, Step 12 Inv 4, Part 2, Step 7

WRITING STANDARDS

Standard	Solids and Liquids Module
Text Types and Purposes	
1. Write opinion pieces in which they introduce the topic or book they are writing about, state an opinion, supply reasons that support the opinion, use linking words (e.g., *because*, *and*, *also*) to connect opinion and reasons, and provide a concluding statement or section.	All investigations provide opportunities for students to write about a science topic, stating their opinion or claim, supported by reasons in answer to the focus questions and in the I-Check assessments. Selected examples Inv 1, Part 3, Step 10; Inv 1, Part 4, Step 13 Inv 2, Part 1, Step 12 Inv 3, Part 1, Step 15 Inv 4, Part 3, Step 11
2. Write informative/explanatory texts in which they introduce a topic, use facts and definitions to develop points, and provide a concluding statement or section.	All investigations provide opportunities for students to write explanatory texts to examine the science topic they are learning. Students write an explanation as part of their answer to the focus question in the I-Check assessments, and in response to the readings. Selected examples Inv 1, Language extension. Make "My Book of Solids" Inv 2, Part 3, Step 15 Inv 3, Part 4, Steps 5, 8-9 Inv 4, Part 5, Step 9
3. Write narratives in which they recount a well elaborated event or short sequence of events, include details to describe actions, thoughts, and feelings, use temporal words to signal event order, and provide a sense of closure.	All investigations provide opportunities for students to write narratives. Students describe their observations and experiences with the science ideas they are exploring. Selected examples Inv 2, Part 4, Step 15 Inv 3, Part 3, Step 11 Inv 4, Part 1, Step 26

Insects and Plants Module	Pebbles, Sand, and Silt Module
All investigations provide opportunities for students to write about a science topic, stating their opinion or claim, supported by reasons in answer to the focus questions and in the I-Check assessments. Selected examples Inv 1, Part 1, Step 16 Inv 2, Part 4, Steps 8, 22 Inv 3, Part 2, Step 17 Inv 4, Part 1, Step 16; Inv 4, Part 4, Step 15	All investigations provide opportunities for students to write about a science topic, stating their opinion or claim, supported by reasons in answer to the focus questions and in the I-Check assessments. Selected examples Inv 2, Part 3, Step 16 Inv 3, Part 5, Step 11
All investigations provide opportunities for students to write explanatory texts to examine the science topic they are learning. Students write an explanation as part of their answer to the focus question in the I-Check assessments, and in response to the readings. Selected examples Inv 2, Part 1, Step 11; Inv 2, Part 2, Step 14 Inv 3, Part 4, Step 20 Inv 4, Part 2, Step 17; Inv 4, Part 3, Step 6 Inv 5, Part 2, Step 5	All investigations provide opportunities for students to write explanatory texts to examine the science topic they are learning. Students write an explanation as part of their answer to the focus question in the I-Check assessments, and in response to the readings. Selected examples Inv 1, Part 1, Step 12; Inv 1, Part 3, Step 12 Inv 2, Part 1, Step 19; Inv 2, Part 2, Steps 10, 11; Inv 2, Part 3, Step 16 Inv 3, Part 5, Step 2 Inv 3, Language extension. Look for rocks everywhere Inv 4, Part 4, Step 4; Inv 4, Language extension. Draw soil profiles
All investigations provide opportunities for students to write narratives. Students describe their observations and experiences with the science ideas they are exploring. Selected examples Inv 1, Part 2, Steps 6, 9, 12 Inv 2, Part 2, Steps 5, 9, 12-14; Inv 2, Part 4, Step 22 Inv 3, Part 1, Step 8; Inv 3, Part 2, Step 17; Inv 3, Part 3, Steps 1-3, 6; Inv 3, Part 4, Step 10; Inv 4, Part 3, Step 6 Inv 4, Language extension. Invent an insect Inv 5, Part 1, Step 13; Inv 5, Part 4, Step 17	All investigations provide opportunities for students to write narratives. Students describe their observations and experiences with the science ideas they are exploring. Selected examples Inv 1, Language extension. Make a rock record book Inv 1, Language extension. Set up a rock store Inv 1, Language extension. Write about magic pebbles Inv 2, Part 2, Step 11 Inv 2, Language extension. Write the journey of your rock Inv 2, Language extension. Write rock stories Inv 3, Part 5, Step 11 Inv 3, Language extension. Make tracks and molds Inv 4, Language extension. Write directions for making soil

WRITING STANDARDS (*continued*)

Standard	Solids and Liquids Module
Production and Distribution of Writing	
5. With guidance and support from adults and peers, focus on a topic and strengthen writing as needed by revising and editing.	The Wrap-Up/Warm-Up section of each investigation part provides the opportunity for students to strengthen their notebook entries by revising and adding in new information. The next–step strategies after taking the I-Check also serve as a method for strengthening writing. Selected examples Inv 1, Part 1, Step 20; Inv 2, Part 1, Step 13; Inv 2, Part 3, Step 11; Inv 3, Part 2, Step 13
6. With guidance and support from adults, use a variety of digital tools to produce and publish writing, including in collaboration with peers.	
7. Participate in shared research and writing projects (e.g., read a number of books on a single topic to produce a report; record science observations).	In every investigation students record their observations in their notebooks. They also write about articles in *FOSS Science Resources*. Selected examples: Inv 1, Part 1, Step 13; Inv 1, Part 2, Step 10; Inv 1, Part 3, Step 10; Inv 1, Part 4, Step 13; Inv 1, Part 5, Step 8; Inv 2, Part 3, Step 6 Inv 3, Part 1, Step 10; Inv 3, Part 5, Step 10 Inv 4, Part 1, Steps 7, 13, 22; Inv 4, Part 2, Step 7; Inv 4, Part 3, Steps 5-9, 11; Inv 4, Part 5, Step 9
Research to Build and Present Knowledge	
8. Recall information from experiences or gather information from provided sources to answer a question.	All investigations provide students with the opportunity to write about their science experiences and record their observations in their science notebooks. Students also take notes and organize information when reading articles in *FOSS Science Resources*. Selected examples Inv 1, Part 1, Steps 13, 17; Inv 1, Part 2, Steps 10-11, 15; Inv 1, Part 3, Step 10; Inv 1, Part 4, Step 13 Inv 2, Part 1, Step 12; Inv 2, Part 2, Step 17; Inv 2, Part 3, Step 15; Inv 2, Part 4, Step 15 Inv 3, Part 3, Steps 11, 12; Inv 3, Part 4, Step 5 Inv 4, Part 1, Step 25; Inv 4, Part 2, Step 7; Inv 4, Part 3, Step 11; Inv 4, Part 4, Step 18

Insects and Plants Module	Pebbles, Sand, and Silt Module
The Wrap-Up/Warm-Up section of each investigation part provides the opportunity for students to strengthen their notebook entries by revising and adding in new information. The next-step strategies after taking the I-Check also serve as a method for strengthening writing. Selected examples Inv 1, Part 2, Step 17; Inv 3, Part 1, Step 10; Inv 4, Part 1, Step 18; Inv 4, Part 2, Step 21; Inv 5, Part 2, Step 7	The Wrap-Up/Warm-Up section of each investigation part provides the opportunity for students to strengthen their notebook entries by revising and adding in new information. The next-step strategies after taking the I-Check also serve as a method for strengthening writing. Selected example Inv 1, Part 4, Step 17
In every investigation students record their observations in their notebooks. They also write about articles in *FOSS Science Resources*. Selected examples Inv 1, Part 1, Step 16; Inv 1, Part 2, Steps 4, 8, 9, 11, 14; Inv 1, Part 3, Steps 9, 10; Inv 1, Science extension. Search for insects Inv 2, Part 1, Steps 17, 18; Inv 2, Part 2, Steps 1, 3-5, 8-9, 13-14; Inv 3, Part 1, Step 7; Inv 3, Part 2, Step 15; Inv 3, Part 3, Steps 2, 3, 6, 9; Inv 3, Part 4, Steps 15-17 Inv 4, Part 1, Steps 6, 16; Inv 4, Part 2, Steps 7-10; Inv 4, Part 3, Steps 2, 8; Inv 5, Part 1, Steps 6, 8, 11, 12	In every investigation students record their observations in their notebooks. They also write about articles in *FOSS Science Resources*. Selected examples Inv 1, Part 5, Step 7 Inv 2, Part 3, Steps 11, 13 Inv 3, Part 1, Steps 3, 4, 7 Inv 4, Part 1, Step 21; Inv 4, Part 2, Steps 17-18; Inv 4, Language extension. Compare soil habitats
All investigations provide students with the opportunity to write about their science experiences and record their observations in their science notebooks. Students also take notes and organize information when reading articles in *FOSS Science Resources*. Selected examples Inv 1, Part 1, Steps 16, 18; Inv 1, Part 2, Step 2; Inv 1, Part 3, Step 9; Inv 2, Part 1, Steps 11, 12; Inv 2, Part 2, Step 14; Inv 2, Part 4, Step 8; Inv 3, Part 1, Step 8; Inv 3, Part 2, Step 17; Inv 3, Part 3, Steps 1, 6, 11; Inv 3, Part 4, Step 20; Inv 4, Part 1, Step 16; Inv 4, Part 2, Step 17; Inv 4, Part 3, Step 6; Inv 4, Part 4, Step 15 Inv 5, Part 1, Step 13; Inv 5, Part 2, Step 5; Inv 5, Part 3, Step 10; Inv 5, Part 4, Step 17	All investigations provide students with the opportunity to write about their science experiences and record their observations in their science notebooks. Students also take notes and organize information when reading articles in *FOSS Science Resources*. Selected examples Inv 1, Part 1, Step 12; Inv 1, Part 2, Step 11; Inv 1, Part 3, Step 12; Inv 1, Part 4, Step 11 Inv 2, Part 1, Step 19; Inv 2, Part 2, Step 7; Inv 2, Part 3, Step 16; Inv 2, Part 4, Steps 15, 22 Inv 3, Part 1, Steps 9, 13; Inv 3, Part 3, Step 11; Inv 3, Part 4, Steps 9, 11; Inv 3, Part 5, Step 11 Inv 4, Part 1, Step 24; Inv 4, Part 2, Step 19

SPEAKING AND LISTENING STANDARDS

Standard	Solids and Liquids Module
Comprehension and Collaboration	
1. Participate in collaborative conversations with diverse partners about *grade 2 topics and texts* with peers and adults in small and larger groups. a. Follow agreed-upon rules for discussions (e.g., gaining the floor in respectful ways, listening to others with care, speaking one at a time about the topics and texts under discussion). b. Build on others' talk in conversations by linking their comments to the remarks of others. c. Ask for clarification and further explanation as needed about the topics and texts under discussion.	All investigations provide students ample opportunities to engage in collaborative discussions. Students discuss before, during, and after the active investigation, when reading articles in the *FOSS Science Resources*, and during the Wrap-Up/Warm-Up section. Selected examples Inv 1, Part 2, Steps 2, 8; Inv 1, Part 3, Step 14; Inv 1, Part 4, Steps 6, 15, 18; Inv 1, Part 5, Step 16; Inv 2, Part 1, Step 13; Inv 2, Part 2, Steps 7, 19; Inv 2, Part 3, Step 17; Inv 3, Part 1, Steps 12, 17; Inv 3, Part 3, Step 11; Inv 3, Part 4, Step 10; Inv 4, Part 3, Steps 9-13; Inv 4, Part 4, Steps 17, 20, 26
2. Recount or describe key ideas or details from a text read aloud or information presented orally or through other media.	All investigations provide opportunities for students to recount or describe ideas and details from the investigations and from reading the articles in *FOSS Science Resources*. This module also includes video discussions. Selected examples Inv 1, Part 2, Steps 16, 17; Inv 1, Part 3, Step 1; Inv 1, Part 4, Steps 11, 15, 24; Inv 2, Part 2, Step 20; Inv 2, Part 3, Step 17; Inv 3, Part 2, Step 2; Inv 3, Part 5, Steps 11-12; Inv 4, Part 1, Steps 1, 19; Inv 4, Part 2, Steps 9, 16; Inv 4, Part 4, Step 25
3. Ask and answer questions about what a speaker says in order to clarify comprehension, gather additional information, or deepen understanding of a topic or issue.	All investigations provide students with the opportunity to ask and answer questions about how they answered the focus question during the Wrap-Up/Warm-Up section. Other opportunities arise when students present information to their group or the whole class. Selected examples Inv 1, Part 1, Step 20; Inv 1, Part 4, Step 20 Inv 2, Part 1, Step 6; Inv 2, Part 3, Steps 9, 17; Inv 2, Part 4, Steps 6, 10, 11, 13 Inv 3, Part 2, Steps 7, 13; Inv 3, Part 3, Steps 7, 10; Inv 3, Part 4, Step 4; Inv 3, Part 5, Steps 7-8 Inv 4, Part 1; Steps 9, 11, 12, 14; Inv 4, Part 3, Step 1; Inv 4, Part 4, Steps 1, 2, 6, 8-10, 15; Inv 4, Part 5, Steps 1-3, 6

Insects and Plants Module	Pebbles, Sand, and Silt Module
All investigations provide students ample opportunities to engage in collaborative discussions. Students discuss before, during, and after the active investigation, when reading articles in the *FOSS Science Resources*, and during the Wrap-Up/Warm-Up section. Selected examples Inv 1, Part 1, Step 18 Inv 2, Part 2, Steps 11-12 Inv 3, Part 2, Step 21; Inv 3, Part 4, Step 18 Inv 4, Part 1, Step 18; Inv 4, Part 2, Steps 20-21 Inv 5, Part 2, Step 6	All investigations provide students ample opportunities to engage in collaborative discussions. Students discuss before, during, and after the active investigation, when reading articles in the *FOSS Science Resources*, and during the Wrap-Up/Warm-Up section. Selected examples Inv 1, Part 4, Step 17; Inv 1, Part 5, Step 3; Inv 2, Part 1, Step 21; Inv 3, Part 2, Steps 10, 15; Inv 3, Part 3, Step 12; Inv 3, Part 4, Steps 3, 13; Inv 4, Part 1, Step 26; Inv 4, Part 2, Step 26; Inv 4, Part 3, Steps 4, 5, 10
All investigations provide opportunities for students to recount or describe ideas and details from the investigations and from reading the articles in *FOSS Science Resources*. This module also includes video discussions. Selected examples Inv 1, Part 1, Steps 18-19 Inv 2, Part 1, Steps 10, 19; Inv 2, Part 2, Steps 11-12, 17; Inv 2, Part 4, Step 21 Inv 3, Part 1, Step 10; Inv 3, Part 2, Step 1 Inv 4, Part 2, Step 20; Inv 5, Part 4, Steps 2, 3	All investigations provide opportunities for students to recount or describe ideas and details from the investigations and from reading the articles in *FOSS Science Resources*. This module also includes video discussions. Selected examples Inv 1, Part 1, Step 15; Inv 1, Part 2, Step 15; Inv 1, Part 3, Steps 1, 11, 17; Inv 1, Part 5, Step 1 Inv 2, Part 2, Step 8; Inv 2, Part 4, Steps 22, 23 Inv 4, Part 3, Step 4 Inv 4, Part 1, Step 10; Inv 4, Part 2, Step 23
All investigations provide students with the opportunity to ask and answer questions about how they answered the focus question during the Wrap-Up/Warm-Up section. Other opportunities arise when students present information to their group or the whole class. Selected examples Inv 1, Part 1, Steps 1, 3, 6, 7; Inv 1, Part 2, Steps 2, 5, 6, 8, 12, 15-17; Inv 1, Part 3, Steps 1, 5, 7; Inv 2, Part 1, Step 1; Inv 2, Part 2, Steps 1-4, 7, 8, 10-15, 20; Inv 2, Part 3, Step 3; Inv 2, Part 4, Steps 2, 14, 18-22; Inv 3, Part 1, Steps 3, 10; Inv 3, Part 2, Steps 1, 4, 13, 22; Inv 3, Part 3, Step 2; Inv 3, Part 4, Steps 3, 10, 13; Inv 4, Part 1, Steps 3, 7, 9, 12; Inv 4, Part 2, Steps 1, 2, 9; Inv 4, Part 4, Steps 1, 3, 9, 11; Inv 5, Part 1, Steps 1, 3, 5; Inv 5, Part 2, Steps 1, 2; Inv 5, Part 3, Steps 2, 3	All investigations provide students with the opportunity to ask and answer questions about how they answered the focus question during the Wrap-Up/Warm-Up section. Other opportunities arise when students present information to their group or the whole class. Selected examples Inv 1, Part 1, Steps 1, 4, 8, 9; Inv 1, Part 2, Steps 5, 7, 8, 14; Inv 1, Part 3, Step 11; Inv 1, Part 4, Steps 1, 3, 7, 9, 14 Inv 2, Part 1, Steps 8, 9, 11, 13-15; Inv 2, Part 3, Steps 6, 8, 9; Inv 2, Part 4, Steps 3, 6-8, 13, 14, 16 Inv 3, Part 1, Steps 1, 4, 6; Inv 3, Part 2, Step 6; Inv 3, Part 3, Steps 1, 2, 8; Inv 3, Part 5, Steps 2, 4; Inv 4, Part 4, Step 5; Inv 3, Language extension. Find out about pottery Inv 4, Part 1, Steps 9, 11, 13, 14, 22; Inv 4, Part 2, Steps 6, 10, 20

SPEAKING AND LISTENING STANDARDS
(*continued*)

Standard	Solids and Liquids Module
4. Tell a story or recount an experience with appropriate facts and relevant, descriptive details, speaking audibly in coherent sentences.	All investigations provide students with the opportunity to report on their results. In the Wrap-Up/Warm-Up section students recount what they did in the investigation and share their answers to the focus question. Students report on what they learn from the text when discussing the articles in *FOSS Science Resources*. Selected examples Inv 1, Part 3, Step 8 Inv 2, Part 2, Step 9; Inv 2, Part 3, Step 20 Inv 3, Part 1, Step 17 Inv 4, Part 2, Steps 1, 2; Inv 4, Part 4, Step 23; Inv 4, Part 5, Step 1
5. Create audio recordings of stories or poems; add drawings or other visual displays to stories or recounts of experiences when appropriate to clarify ideas, thoughts, and feelings.	Students add drawings to their notebook entries to clarify their ideas and answers to the focus questions. Inv 1, Part 1, Step 13; Inv 1, Part 4, Steps 21, 23 Inv 3, Part 2, Step 11 Inv 4, Part 1, Step 26
6. Produce complete sentences when appropriate to task and situation in order to provide requested detail or clarification.	All investigations provide students with the opportunity to speak in complete sentences to provide details or clarification about their science learning. Sentence frames are provided for those students that need scaffolding. Selected examples Inv 1, Part 1, Step 13; Inv 1, Part 2, Step 7; Inv 1, Part 5, Step 16 Inv 2, Part 2, Step 19 Inv 3, Part 2, Step 11 Inv 4, Part 4, Steps 18, 26

Presentation of Knowledge and Ideas

Insects and Plants Module	Pebbles, Sand, and Silt Module
All investigations provide students with the opportunity to report on their results. In the Wrap-Up/Warm-Up section students recount what they did in the investigation and share their answers to the focus question. Students report on what they learn from the text when discussing the articles in *FOSS Science Resources*. Selected examples Inv 2, Part 2, Step 23; Inv 2, Part 3, Step 14; Inv 2, Part 4, Step 17 Inv 3, Part 3, Step 14 Inv 5, Part 1, Step 16	All investigations provide students with the opportunity to report on their results. In the Wrap-Up/Warm-Up section students recount what they did in the investigation and share their answers to the focus question. Students report on what they learn from the text when discussing the articles in *FOSS Science Resources*. Selected examples Inv 2, Part 2, Steps 11, 12; Inv 2, Part 3, Step 21 Inv 3, Part 1, Step 13 Inv 4, Part 2, Step 7; Inv 4, Part 4, Steps 1, 5
Students add drawings to their notebook entries to clarify their ideas and answers to the focus questions. Inv 2, Part 2, Step 14; Inv 2, Part 3, Step 12; Inv 2, Part 4, Steps 16, 21 Inv 3, Part 3, Step 1; Inv 3, Part 4, Steps 10-11 Inv 5, Part 2, Step 1; Inv 5, Part 3, Step 17; Inv 5, Language extension. Diagram life cycles	Students add drawings to their notebook entries to clarify their ideas and answers to the focus questions. Inv 2, Part 2, Step 10; Inv 2, Part 4, Step 31 Inv 4, Part 3, Step 11; Inv 4, Part 4, Steps 6-7
All investigations provide students with the opportunity to speak in complete sentences to provide details or clarification about their science learning. Sentence frames are provided for those students that need scaffolding. Selected examples Inv 1, Part 1, Step 18 Inv 2, Part 2, Step 11; Inv 2, Part 3, Step 12 Inv 3, Part 1, Step 8; Inv 3, Part 2, Steps 13, 17; Inv 3, Part 3, Step 1; Inv 3, Part 4, Step 10 Inv 4, Part 1, Steps 7, 12	All investigations provide students with the opportunity to speak in complete sentences to provide details or clarification about their science learning. Sentence frames are provided for those students that need scaffolding. Selected examples Inv 2, Part 2, Step 11; Inv 2, Part 3, Step 16

FOSS and Common Core ELA — Grade 2

LANGUAGE STANDARDS

Standard	Solids and Liquids Module
Conventions of Standard English 1. Demonstrate command of the conventions of standard English grammar and usage when writing or speaking. a. Use collective nouns (e.g., *group*). b. Form and use frequently occurring irregular plural nouns (e.g., *feet, children, teeth, mice, fish*). c. Use reflexive pronouns (e.g., *myself, ourselves*). d. Form and use the past tense of frequently occurring irregular verbs (e.g., *sat, hid, told*). e. Use adjectives and adverbs, and choose between them depending on what is to be modified. f. Produce, expand, and rearrange complete simple and compound sentences (e.g., *The boy watched the movie; The little boy watched the movie; The action movie was watched by the little boy*).	All investigations provide opportunities for students to apply the conventions of English grammar when writing and speaking. Selected examples Inv 1, Part 2, Step 7; Inv 1, Part 3, Step 5 Inv 2, Part 2, Step 19 Inv 3, Part 1, Step 15 Inv 4, Part 2, Step 17; Inv 4, Part 4, Step 26
2. Demonstrate command of the conventions of standard English capitalization, punctuation, and spelling when writing. a. Capitalize holidays, product names, and geographic names. b. Use commas in greetings and closings of letters. c. Use an apostrophe to form contractions and frequently occurring possessives. d. Generalize learned spelling patterns when writing words (e.g., cage→badge; boy→boil). e. Consult reference materials, including beginning dictionaries, as needed to check and correct spellings.	All investigations provide opportunities for students to demonstrate command of the conventions of standard English capitalization, punctuation, and spelling when writing in their science notebooks and the I-Checks.
Knowledge of Language 3. Use knowledge of language and its conventions when writing, speaking, reading, or listening. a. Compare formal and informal uses of English.	All investigations provide opportunities for students to use their knowledge of language and its conventions when writing in their science notebooks, discussing the investigation, and reading the articles in *FOSS Science Resources*. Selected examples Inv 1, Part 3, Step 14 Inv 2, Part 2, Step 7 Inv 3, Part 1, Step 12 Inv 4, Part 2, Step 17; Inv 4, Part 4, Step 26

Full Option Science System

Language Standards

Insects and Plants Module	Pebbles, Sand, and Silt Module
All investigations provide opportunities for students to apply the conventions of English grammar when writing and speaking. Selected examples Inv 1, Part 1, Steps 16, 18; Inv 1, Part 2, Step 5 Inv 2, Part 1, Steps 11, 12; Inv 2, Part 4, Steps 8, 22 Inv 3, Part 3, Step 1; Inv 3, Part 4, Steps 18, 20 Inv 4, Part 1, Steps 7, 12, 16; Inv 4, Part 3, Step 12; Inv 4, Part 4, Step 15	All investigations provide opportunities for students to apply the conventions of English grammar when writing and speaking. Selected examples Inv 2, Part 2, Step 11; Inv 2, Part 3, Step 16
All investigations provide opportunities for students to demonstrate command of the conventions of standard English capitalization, punctuation, and spelling when writing in their science notebooks and the I-Checks.	All investigations provide opportunities for students to demonstrate command of the conventions of standard English capitalization, punctuation, and spelling when writing in their science notebooks and the I-Checks.
All investigations provide opportunities for students to use their knowledge of language and its conventions when writing in their science notebooks, discussing the investigation, and reading the articles in *FOSS Science Resources*. Selected examples Inv 1, Part 2, Steps 5, 10 Inv 2, Part 2, Steps 1-2, 7; Inv 2, Part 3, Step 14; Inv 2, Part 4, Step 22 Inv 3, Part 3, Step 1; Inv 3, Part 4, Step 18 Inv 4, Part 1, Steps 7, 12 Inv 5, Part 1, Step 3	All investigations provide opportunities for students to use their knowledge of language and its conventions when writing in their science notebooks, discussing the investigation, and reading the articles in *FOSS Science Resources*. Selected examples Inv 1, Part 5, Step 3 Inv 2, Part 3, Step 16 Inv 3, Part 1, Step 8

LANGUAGE STANDARDS (*continued*)

Standard	Solids and Liquids Module
Vocabulary Acquisition and Use 4. Determine or clarify the meaning of unknown and multiple-meaning words and phrases based on *grade 2 reading and content*, choosing flexibly from an array of strategies. a. Use sentence-level context as a clue to the meaning of a word or phrase. b. Determine the meaning of the new word formed when a known prefix is added to a known word (e.g., *happy/unhappy, tell/retell*). c. Use a known root word as a clue to the meaning of an unknown word with the same root (e.g., *addition, additional*). d. Use knowledge of the meaning of individual words to predict the meaning of compound words (e.g., *birdhouse, lighthouse, housefly, bookshelf, notebook, bookmark*). e. Use glossaries and beginning dictionaries, both print and digital, to determine or clarify the meaning of words and phrases.	All investigations provide opportunities for students to determine or clarify meaning of academic and science-specific words and phrases while discussing the investigations and articles in *FOSS Science Resources*. Selected examples Inv 1, Part 1, Steps 16, 19 Inv 2, Part 2, Step 6 Inv 3, Part 1, Steps 1, 3, 13 Inv 4, Part 2, Step 15
5. Demonstrate understanding of word relationships and nuances in word meanings. a. Identify real-life connections between words and their use (e.g., describe foods that are *spicy* or *juicy*). b. Distinguish shades of meaning among closely related verbs (e.g., *toss, throw, hurl*) and closely related adjectives (e.g., *thin, slender, skinny, scrawny*).	All investigations provide students with opportunities to demonstrate understanding of word relationships (e.g., concept maps) and nuances of certain words that have a specific meaning in science, such as **matter, property, material, argument, claim, evidence, transparent, gravity, level, mixture, particle, model,** and **dissolve.** Selected examples Inv 1, Part 1, Step 17; Inv 1, Part 2, Step 15 Inv 2, Part 1, Step 10; Inv 2, Part 2, Step 6 Inv 3, Part 3, Steps 7, 12; Inv 3, Part 5, Step 7 Inv 4, Part 2, Step 15; Inv 4, Part 4, Steps 8-10, 15, 17
6. Use words and phrases acquired through conversations, reading and being read to, and responding to texts, including using adjectives and adverbs to describe (e.g., *When other kids are happy that makes me happy*).	All investigations provide opportunities for students to use new science words and phrases acquired through science discussions and readings. Science vocabulary words are in bold when they are first introduced to students in *FOSS Science Resources*. Students also review the vocabulary in the *Review vocabulary* section for each part of each investigation. Selected examples Inv 1, Part 2, Step 9; Inv 1, Part 4, Step 13; Inv 1, Part 5, Step 16; Inv 2, Part 2, Step 13; Inv 2, Part 3, Steps 10, 20 Inv 3, Part 1, Step 13; Inv 4, Part 1, Steps 20-21, 25-26; Inv 4, Part 2, Step 6; Inv 4, Part 4, Step 21

Insects and Plants Module	Pebbles, Sand, and Silt Module
All investigations provide opportunities for students to determine or clarify meaning of academic and science-specific words and phrases while discussing the investigations and articles in *FOSS Science Resources.* Selected examples Inv 1, Part 1, Step 18 Inv 2, Part 2, Step 20 Inv 3, Part 2, Step 19 Inv 4, Part 2, Step 13 Inv 5, Part 3, Steps 8, 17	All investigations provide opportunities for students to determine or clarify meaning of academic and science-specific words and phrases while discussing the investigations and articles in *FOSS Science Resources.* Selected examples Inv 1, Language extension. Create a property map Inv 2, Part 2, Step 8 Inv 3, Part 5, Step 12 Inv 4, Part 2, Step 8
All investigations provide students with opportunities to demonstrate understanding of word relationships (e.g., concept maps) and nuances of certain words that have a specific meaning in science, such as **insect, segment, stage, bud, stem, fruit, bug, evidence,** and **waste.** Selected examples Inv 1, Part 1, Step 19; Inv 1, Part 2, Step 16 Inv 2, Part 3, Step 12; Inv 2, Part 4, Step 22 Inv 3, Part 3, Step 3 Inv 4, Part 2, Steps 8, 9, 11-15 Inv 5, Part 3, Steps 12, 18	All investigations provide students with opportunities to demonstrate understanding of word relationships (e.g., concept maps) and nuances of certain words that have a specific meaning in science, such as **dull, data, group, pattern, property, weathering, particle, cobble, plain, screen, settle, sink, clay, pebble, model, fine, matrix, natural resources, decay, gas, retain, soil, solid,** and **liquid.** Selected examples Inv 1, Part 1, Step 4; Inv 1, Part 5, Step 3 Inv 2, Part 3, Steps 6, 19; Inv 2, Part 4, Steps 19, 31 Inv 3, Part 1, Step 8; Inv 3, Part 3, Step 10 Inv 4, Part 2, Step 20; Inv 4, Part 3, Steps 6, 10
All investigations provide opportunities for students to use new science words and phrases acquired through science discussions and readings. Science vocabulary words are in bold when they are first introduced to students in *FOSS Science Resources.* Students also review the vocabulary in the *Review vocabulary* section for each part of each investigation. Selected examples Inv 1, Part 1, Step 14; Inv 1, Part 2, Steps 10, 16, 17 Inv 2, Part 2, Steps 2, 20, 21, 23; Inv 2, Part 3, Step 6 Inv 4, Part 1, Step 7 Inv 5, Part 4, Step 3	All investigations provide opportunities for students to use new science words and phrases acquired through science discussions and readings. Science vocabulary words are in bold when they are first introduced to students in *FOSS Science Resources.* Students also review the vocabulary in the *Review vocabulary* section for each part of each investigation. Selected examples Inv 1, Part 1, Step 14; Inv 1, Part 5, Step 3 Inv 2, Part 1, Steps 15, 16, 18; Inv 2, Part 2, Step 8 Inv 3, Part 1, Step 8; Inv 3, Part 2, Steps 6, 7 Inv 3, Part 3, Step 10 Inv 4, Part 3, Steps 4, 5

FOSS and Common Core Math – Grade 2

FOSS and Common Core Math — Grade 2

Contents

INTRODUCTION

The adoption of the Common Core State Standards for Mathematics calls for shifts in focus, coherence, and rigor. The teaching of the standards should be focused on the important content, coherent from one grade level to the next, and rigorous in requiring conceptual understanding, fluency, and application. Within this area of application, FOSS provides fertile ground for the use of mathematics.

The FOSS Program integrates mathematics with science in two ways throughout the grade 2 modules. In active investigations, students apply mathematics during data gathering and analysis. In addition, the Interdisciplinary Extensions at the end of each investigation usually include a math problem of the week. These problems enhance the science learning by providing hypothetical data for students to analyze or in some way relate to the context of the investigation. The notes explain for the teacher the problem and describe how students might approach its solution. The problems are prepared for distribution to students on duplication masters in the Teacher Masters chapter of *Teacher Resources*.

This chapter gives an overview of how FOSS addresses the Common Core State Standards for Mathematics through science. It also points out specific instances in which students exercise those skills during science instruction.

Mathematical Practices

Mathematical practices consist of eight processes and proficiencies that are important for all students.

1. Make sense of problems and persevere in solving them.

2. Reason abstractly and quantitatively.

3. Construct viable arguments and critique the reasoning of others.

4. Model with mathematics.

5. Use appropriate tools strategically.

6. Attend to precision.

7. Look for and make use of structure.

8. Look for and express regularity in repeated reasoning.

Within the context of science, students use some of these mathematical practices on a regular basis. According to *Next Generation Science Standards* (volume 2, appendix L, p. 138), the three CCSSM practice standards most directly relevant to science are:

• MP.2. Reason abstractly and quantitatively.

• MP.4. Model with mathematics.

• MP.5. Use appropriate tools strategically.

When students reason abstractly and quantitatively and model with mathematics, they are using math in context. They work with symbols and their meanings and represent and solve word problems. Students choose and correctly use the available tools to collect data and solve problems. In the grade 2 modules, students engage with these three practices during the active investigation and by completing the problems at the end of each investigation. Here are some examples.

In solving Math problem B for Investigation 1 of the **Insects and Plants Module**, students make direct comparisons and use their ability to use and create a graph. In order to solve this, students reason quantitatively and use mathematics in the context of science. They use the data about larvae, pupae, and adult mealworms and model how the population changes overnight and create a second graph.

In the **Pebbles, Sand, and Silt Module**, students are presented with data about the number of rocks various students have found during a rock hunt. Students model using addition and subtration strategies to determine what happens under different situations of combining and comparing rocks. The story problems provide opportunities for students to ulitilze tools to determine the solutions to one- and two-step problems.

In the **Solids and Liquids Module**, students are asked to reason abstractly to determine the receipe of a soft drink. This requires students to manipulate the receipe either abstractly by using number sentences such as 4 + 4 + 4 + 4 or using concrete counters to respresent the spoons, ounces or drops of the different ingredients.

Mathematical Content

The mathematical content in second grade is organized around four concepts.

- Operations and algebraic thinking

- Number and operations in base ten

- Measurement and data

- Geometry

The following pages have a table that identifies the opportunities to engage students in developing these mathematical concepts as well as those learned in grade 1. It lists some of the math content for first and second grades and points out relevant opportunities in the three FOSS modules to address the math standards for grade 2.

OPERATIONS AND ALGEBRAIC THINKING

Standard	Solids and Liquids Module
Represent and solve problems involving addition and subtraction.	
1. Use addition and subtraction within 100 to solve one- and two-step word problems involving situations of adding to, taking from, putting together, taking apart, and comparing, with unknowns in all positions, e.g., by using drawings and equations with a symbol for the unknown number to represent the problem.	Inv 4, Math problem B
Add and subtract within 20.	
2. Fluently add and subtract within 20 using mental strategies. By end of Grade 2, know from memory all sums of two one-digit numbers.	
Work with equal groups of objects to gain foundations for multiplication.	
4. Use addition to find the total number of objects arranged in rectangular arrays with up to 5 rows and up to 5 columns; write an equation to express the total as a sum of equal addends.	

Common Core State Standards for Mathematics (National Governors Association Center for Best Practices and Council of Chief State School Officers, 2010).

Insects and Plants Module	Pebbles, Sand, and Silt Module
Inv 2, Math problem B	Inv 1, Math problems A and B Inv 4, Math problem
Inv 1, Math problem A	Inv 3, Math problem A
	Inv 3, Math problem B

NUMBER AND OPERATIONS IN BASE TEN

Grade 2	Standard	Solids and Liquids Module
	Understand place value.	
	2. Count within 1000; skip-count by 5s, 10s, and 100s.	
	Use place value understanding and properties of operations to add and subtract.	
	5. Fluently add and subtract within 100 using strategies based on place value, properties of operations, and/or the relationship between addition and subtraction.	

Insects and Plants Module	Pebbles, Sand, and Silt Module
Inv 3, Math problem A	
Inv 1, Math problem A Inv 3, Math problem A	

MEASUREMENT AND DATA

Standard	Solids and Liquids Module
Measure lengths indirectly and by iterating length units.	
1. Order three objects by length; compare the lengths of two objects indirectly by using a third object.	Inv 3, Part 4, Step 5, Focus question: What is a general rule for using screens to separate a mixture of small objects?
Measure and estimate lengths in standard units.	
1. Measure the length of an object by selecting and using appropriate tools such as rulers, yardsticks, meter sticks, and measuring tapes.	Inv 1, Part 4, Step 9, Test and measure towers
Work with time and money.	
7. Tell and write time from analog and digital clocks to the nearest five minutes, using a.m. and p.m.	Inv 4, Math problem A
8. Solve word problems involving dollar bills, quarters, dimes, nickels, and pennies, using $ and ¢ symbols appropriately. *Example: If you have 2 dimes and 3 pennies, how many cents do you have?*	Inv 2, Math problem
Represent and interpret data.	
9. Generate measurement data by measuring lengths of several objects to the nearest whole unit, or by making repeated measurements of the same object. Show the measurements by making a line plot, where the horizontal scale is marked off in whole-number units.	
10. Draw a picture graph and a bar graph (with single-unit scale) to represent a data set with up to four categories. Solve simple put-together, take-apart, and compare problems using information presented in a bar graph.	Inv 3, Math problem A

Grade 1 / *Grade 2*

Insects and Plants Module	Pebbles, Sand, and Silt Module
Inv 2, Part 2, Step 9, Record in science notebook Inv 2, Part 2, Step 14, Answer the focus question Inv 2, Part 3, Step 8, Chart plant growth	
Inv 4, Math problems A and B	Inv 2, Math problems A and B
Inv 2, Part 3, Step 8, Chart plant growth	
Inv 1, Math problem B Inv 3, Math problem B Inv 3, Math extension. Graph variations in your class	Inv 1, Math extension. Graph rock sorts Inv 2, Part 1, Step 20, Create a graph

GEOMETRY

Standard	Solids and Liquids Module
Reason with shapes and their attributes.	
1. Recognize and draw shapes having specified attributes, such as a given number of angles or a given number of equal faces. Identify triangles, quadrilaterals, pentagons, hexagons, and cubes.	Inv 1, Math problem A

Insects and Plants Module	Pebbles, Sand, and Silt Module
	Inv 1, Part 5, Step 3, Introduce sorting activities

Taking FOSS Outdoors

Taking FOSS Outdoors

If we want children to flourish, to become truly empowered, then let us allow them to love the earth before we ask them to save it.

David Sobel, *Beyond Ecophobia*

INTRODUCTION

During its first 20 years, FOSS focused on classroom science. The primary goal was to develop a scientifically literate population with an ever-growing knowledge of the natural world and the interactions and organizational models that govern and explain it. In recent years, it has become clear that we have a larger responsibility to the students we touch with our program. We have to extend classroom learning into the field to bring the science concepts and principles to life. Applying concepts explored in the classroom to another setting, a real-world one in the schoolyard, happens to be effective for academic achievement, but it is also important for students' personal well-being.

In the process of validating classroom learning among the schoolyard trees and shrubs, down in the weeds on the asphalt, and in the sky overhead, students will develop a relationship with nature. It is our relationship with natural systems that allows us to care deeply for these systems. In order for students in our schools today to save Earth, and save it they must, they first have to feel the pulse, smell the breath, and hear the music of nature. So pack up your explorer's kit, throw open the door, and join us. We're taking FOSS outdoors.

Contents

WHAT DOES FOSS LOOK LIKE OUTDOORS?

Visualize taking FOSS outdoors: Students exit the classroom in an orderly fashion, their direction and purpose undeterred by the joyful sounds of other students at recess. With focused enthusiasm, the band of young scientists moves toward the edge of the schoolyard. Each student is carrying something, maybe a clipboard for recording, a container for collecting, or a hand lens for observing. Students reach their destination and quickly form a sharing circle. After a brief orientation, students disperse and begin searching the tall grass along the chain-link fence. All are independently recording in their science notebooks, and all are on task. The teacher moves about with intention, speaking to a few students at a time. After several more minutes of this work, the teacher rings a chime. Students freeze, raise one arm, and look at her. She rings the chime again. Students leave their materials in their spots and re-form their sharing circle with their teacher for discussion or additional instructions.

This scenario could be anywhere in the country with a regular classroom teacher using any of the FOSS modules. Taking FOSS outdoors is a natural extension of the classroom work. It looks and feels a lot like standard FOSS activities. Many of the routines you use inside the classroom can be implemented outdoors as well. Success, however, does depend on a few specialized skills and specific preparation to maximize outdoor teaching efficiency.

Expect the enthusiasm, participation, engagement, group discussions, and effort on notebook entries to be heightened during and after an outdoor experience. Even the simplest outdoor activities create a surge of positive energy. It is difficult to determine whether the enthusiasm and commitment students exhibit when doing FOSS outdoors comes from the physical movement needed to get to the outdoor space, from exercising content they already know in a different setting, or simply from the joy of being outdoors. Expect students to be a bit louder and more excited when they are learning in the schoolyard. The enlarged space allows for this expansion in energy level, which benefits some students immensely. All students benefit from applying and extending their science and engineering practices and content knowledge to the real-world setting of the schoolyard.

GOALS AND OBJECTIVES

The three program goals set down 20 years ago still serve FOSS well. They are: (1) scientific literacy for all students, (2) instructional efficiency and support for teachers, and (3) systemic reform.

The march into the schoolyard has three objectives that relate to the goal for students. First, the outdoor activities **continue and extend the learning** that starts in the classroom. The outdoor activities provide more experience with the content and additional opportunities to practice skills and techniques developed in the classroom.

Second, venturing out provides opportunities for students to discover **applications and examples of classroom content and concepts**. The classroom activities work well for developing sound conceptual science knowledge. That knowledge, however, is constrained by the context in which the concepts are taught. For students to take the next level of ownership of that knowledge, they need to see how it applies and generalizes in the broader context of the world. Leaving the classroom context with a head full of new ideas and new tools for observation enriches the learning.

The third objective is to **connect students with nature**. On the boundaries of the planned, structured experiences are the intangibles that may spark a new relationship with natural systems. It may start with a multisensory experience in the native environment—wind, wet, cold, sunshine, plants, insects, on and on—and advance to an awareness of the diversity of resources surrounding the school. It might evolve into a consciousness of place, followed by a flood of questions about the structure, organization, and operation of the schoolyard ecosystem. When students bond with nature, they have accepted a precious gift, and we have accomplished something important.

MANAGING SPACE

FOSS outdoor activities are designed to be successful in a diversity of schoolyards. Some schoolyards are covered in asphalt, while others have been transformed into thoughtfully-designed outdoor learning environments. Some include large, grassy areas without trees, and others are covered with mulch. One outdoor space may be circled by a variety of mature trees; the next may have recently planted maples and pines scattered about. The space may reflect thoughtful attention or neglect. Nevertheless, FOSS believes that bringing students into the fresh air under a changing sky, into the available outdoor space, will awaken their well-being and stimulate their understanding of science concepts.

Choosing Outdoor Spaces

Whether your school's landscape is wild, manicured, or asphalt, there are more options for outdoor learning spaces than might initially meet the eye. This section will help you choose the best spaces near your school for the FOSS outdoor activity.

Before choosing your outdoor study areas, get to know your outdoor spaces. Look closely at all areas surrounding the school building—even places that students do not normally go. Many seemingly uninteresting

monoculture fields are flourishing with a diversity of different grass species and other small flowering plants. Consider the pile of leaves that blew into a corner of your schoolyard; a crack in the concrete; or the ragged, weedy edge of the field where the lawn mower doesn't reach. These are places that provide small animals with what they need—food, shelter, water, and space. Transition zones where vegetation changes from shrubbery to lawn or garden to field can present interesting study sites. As you ponder the learning possibilities in and around your schoolyard, consider these characteristics.

Accessibility. You should be able to walk from your classroom to your outdoor site in 2–5 minutes. Sites farther than 10 minutes away can be considered for special outings, but are not realistic for frequent access, given the time constraints of a typical school day. Check out physical access if you have students whose mobility requires consideration. Be aware of hazardous surfaces (water, ice, or debris) and caution students to be careful.

Purpose. Determine the space needs of the activity. Some activities will require open space, such as a field or blacktop. Other activities work better if students have a more diverse landscape with varying environmental conditions (temperature, light intensity, wind). Some activities require a variety of human-made materials to measure or test for certain properties (such as metal structures to test for magnetism). Different areas will serve different needs.

Size. The space should be large enough for the class to work comfortably but small enough for you to supervise all students easily. You always need to be able to see all your students, and your students need to be close enough to hear you and your attention signal.

Boundaries. For any space you intend to use, make sure you have clearly defined the boundaries before heading outdoors with your students. Ideally, the landscape will be helpful. For example, stay between the sidewalk and the tree line. If natural markers are not present, you may need to bring along traffic cones or their equivalent to define limits. In general, consider if there are any distractions or hazards, such as debris, poisonous plants, or human traffic.

Fostering and Maintaining Diversity

For life science and earth science studies, ideally you want your site to have a variety of living and dead plant matter, and a range of surface features and environmental conditions. Survey your site to see if it includes places that have survived unmanaged. Even a small wild zone along a fence or behind the maintenance area or an adjacent field can be a valuable resource. It is important for students to see that living things carry on, even in the city, without human assistance.

Enhancing your schoolyard. You may be able to secure a small section of the schoolyard lawn from the school custodian, gardener or grounds keeper, and allow it to go feral to compare it to the adjacent managed school grounds. Consult with your principal to see if this can be arranged.

Another way to enhance biodiversity is to encourage decomposition by letting fallen leaves and/or lawn clippings to remain on an area of soil over the winter. This gives worms and other decomposers something to eat, which, in turn, provides food for everything else. Make sure all necessary parties are aware of your intentions to leave an area untouched. If you find that you need administrative permission, consider ways to contain and mark the unkempt (but not unloved) area so that it clearly represents an intentional project.

Tread lightly. Your schoolyard study areas will potentially experience some user impact. It is important to teach students to minimize their environmental footprint. Otherwise, the living things they disturb might decline or seek a safer place to live. Unless the class is intentionally collecting study specimens, nothing natural should be picked up or removed from the area. This is a good opportunity to introduce the "leave no trace" philosophy, which, in an effort to preserve an area for recreation, encourages us to leave natural objects as we find them.

At some schools, the outdoor space is used by so many classrooms that a system is needed to schedule outdoor activities. A sign-up sheet can be used to reserve outdoor spaces just as is done to reserve other school resources, such as a computer cart. Check the site the morning before taking the class outdoors to make sure the area is ready for students to investigate.

Weather

Weather can present great challenges and exceptional experiences. Inclement weather can provide an excellent opportunity to study environmental concepts: water drainage, wind impact, plant and animal survival adaptations. (There is nothing like being out in a snowstorm to appreciate the value of insulation!) Making extra preparations to study out in the elements has value. If the activity can be undertaken with some assurance of success, go for it. Over time, students acclimate to all sorts of weather and will actually look forward to the challenge of going out in weather.

Clothing. The right gear at the right time can make all the difference. Baseball caps stored at school can work well in a light rain and are often essential as sun protection in warmer climates. Baseball caps in a light rain are especially helpful for students who wear glasses. If possible, invest in a set of rain ponchos to make it possible to go out in wet weather. Communicate regularly with students and family members about upcoming outdoor experiences so that students come to school prepared to work in the outdoor study area.

Wind. A stiff breeze can fling your materials into disarray or send notebooks flying. If you anticipate wind, discuss ways to keep materials from blowing away (such as using natural paperweights or taping down nonliving specimens). If there is a protected area where you and your class can take shelter briefly, the activity can continue. You may have to chase down a couple of notebook sheets before students become accustomed to securing papers and other light materials.

Safety and Comfort

Be prepared for the unexpected. Insect stings (ants, bees, wasps, mosquitoes) can be alarmingly painful for young students, particularly if they have not been stung before. Although extremely unlikely in a schoolyard, have a plan developed with students in advance as to how to retreat with purpose if someone accidentally disturbs a nest. You should already know who is allergic and who has never been stung before.

Skin-irritating plants (poison oak, poison ivy, poison sumac, nettles) can certainly put a damper on a field trip. Take a moment, and get to know your local irritants and toxic plants. The rule "leaves of three, let it be" works only for poison ivy and poison oak. Poison sumac has 7–13 leaves on a branch. Stinging nettle feels much like being stung by a jellyfish and can be very frightening for students who have never experienced it. Often, the irritation subsides within a few minutes; do not treat irritated skin with bleach or rubbing alcohol.

Poison Oak   **Poison Ivy**   **Poison Sumac**

Lyme disease is a treatable bacterial infection, carried by deer ticks. It is present throughout the country, but is particularly present in eastern states. It is possible to get sick without finding a tick bite. If you or your students experience flulike symptoms that are severe enough to see a doctor, make sure that doctor is aware of any outdoor exposure.

If you are out and about in tick country, tuck pant legs into socks and take a few minutes at the end of the trip to pair up and look for obvious ticks on clothing and on the neck and shoulders of a partner.

▶ **SAFETY NOTE**
Refer to FOSSweb, Teaching Tools, Taking FOSS Outdoors for a Tick Awareness letter you may want to send home to parents.

MANAGING TIME
When to Teach

When you start a new module, anticipate when you might want to go outdoors, and schedule the time. The At-a-Glance chart in each investigation can help with this planning.

Time of year. If possible, plan the time of year when you will teach particular modules. In the northern tier, life science and earth science modules would be best in the fall or spring. In the southern tier, it might be best to teach life science modules in the winter when it is not uncomfortably hot during the day. Good times to coordinate your outdoor activities with the school calendar include minimum days or other disruptions to the regular schedule, days just before or after school vacations, and days following district testing.

Time of day. Consider the time of day you teach your activities. Established schedules are often difficult to alter, but you might find it advantageous to do so. If you do a lot of seat work in the mornings, you may want to break the routine occasionally with an outdoor activity. Students will return to the classroom refreshed and ready to focus on the next seated activity you have planned.

If you live in a climate where it gets really hot during the school day, you might want to teach outdoors early in the day. Conversely, if you live in a cold climate, you might want to do your winter outdoor activities midday. If you're looking for wildlife (birds, insects, mammals), the best time to go outdoors might be in the morning.

If you plan to use a part of the schoolyard that is heavily populated at predictable times during the day (lunch, physical education), plan to venture out at a time when other activities are minimal.

Stay flexible. If you are studying the **Water and Climate Module**, for example, be prepared to dash out if it rains or snows. One of the delights of outdoor education is going out when nature is putting on a show. Inquiring minds rush out for the experience when timid observers retreat.

Specific times. Some activities require a sunny day. Measuring shadows, solar water heaters, and solar cell investigations require sunshine. It can be tricky to move on without completing specific observations or experiments. Be creative. You may need to proceed with the module and return to the sunny-day activity when the Sun finally comes out.

Instructional Time

An outdoor activity might require 15 minutes, or it might require an hour. Only part of the time budgeted for outdoor learning is actually spent interacting with the schoolyard terrain, plants, and animals. The rest is management.

Travel time. It will take perhaps 10 minutes from the announcement that it is time to decamp for the schoolyard and the time you arrive there. It will take several minutes to describe and distribute materials, get the appropriate clothing, line up, and travel in an orderly fashion to the designated location. Travel back to the classroom will take another 3–4 minutes.

Instructions. Outdoors, students form a sharing circle. It will take 2–4 minutes to review rules, set the boundaries for the activity, describe the challenge, and distribute materials.

Investigation time. Students break into pairs or groups to engage in the outdoor investigation. This might be as short as 8–10 minutes or as long as 30–40 minutes.

Wrap-up. Students return to the sharing circle to share and discuss their discoveries for several minutes.

Classroom follow-up. Frequently, students bring artifacts back to class to display in a classroom museum or to set up for further observation.

Some outdoor activities call for more flexible allocations of time. An activity may call for setup early in the day with periodic monitoring or measuring throughout the day.

▶ SAFETY NOTE
Students should not disturb or collect live organisms in their natural habitats unless instructed to do so by the teacher.

MANAGING MATERIALS

When students step onto the schoolyard, they are field scientists. In the field, there is no lab bench where investigations can be set up, and there is no ready supply of materials. The field equipment must be minimal, portable, and durable so that it can be easily and safely transported from the classroom and back.

Field Equipment

A student's outdoor bag will contain the specific materials needed for the activity of the day as well as some core necessities, such as a hand lens and a writing tool.

Student outdoor bags might contain these basics.

- Pencils/pens

- Hand lens on brightly colored string or yarn

- Colored pencils or crayons

- Measuring tape

- Vials with caps

- Clipboard or notebook

- Seat pad

Note that pens and pencils each have drawbacks: pencil points break, and pen ink freezes in extremely cold weather. Seat pads can simply be several sheets of newspaper covered with a plastic bag.

Your basic teacher's outdoor equipment bag will include a few backup student materials and some items for helping with management.

- Extra pencils, pens, hand lenses, vials, and cups

- Attention signal (chime, whistle, or cowbell)

- Tissues and paper towels

- Basic first-aid kit (adhesive bandages)

- Phone (if leaving the school grounds)

- Student class list (particularly if you teach more than one class) with appropriate student health information and/or permission slips if away from school.

Transporting Materials

Getting materials to and from the outdoor site is a shared responsibility. Students will carry their personal equipment, and class materials can be distributed among students or tackled as a teacher task. Students always carry something to the outdoor site, even when it would be easier for you to carry everything. This is a subtle reminder that students are heading out for science, not recess. A hand lens serves as such a token.

Some teachers prefer to have students carry only their clipboards or notebooks and pencils, while the teachers carry all the field equipment in a canvas shopping bag or milk crate to the outdoor home base. Other teachers use a wagon or wheelie crate to transport the equipment. After teaching a few outdoor activities, you will discover what works best for you. Students will get excited when they see you preparing your transport system for an outdoor activity.

Water. Water is often used during outdoor activities. If you are lucky, there will be a tap near your study site. More likely, you will carry water from the school building. Recycled plastic jugs with screw caps and smaller bottles with screw caps are good vessels.

At times, you will want open containers of water, such as buckets or basins (for washing rocks, cleaning containers, and so on). Half-filled buckets can be carried a short distance, but basins should be carried empty and filled from jugs.

You rarely have to bring water back inside. Recycle leftover water by watering schoolyard plants. Make this practice overt to help students develop respect for this vital natural resource.

Creating Outdoor Tools

A sturdy writing surface is essential for science in the schoolyard. A bound notebook (composition book) is excellent. A serviceable clipboard can be made from a piece of cardboard and a binder clip. Use a paper cutter to cut sturdy cardboard slightly larger than a sheet of notebook paper. Place a medium-size binder clip at the top and a large elastic band around the bottom (to keep the paper from flapping up). Tie a pencil on a brightly colored string to the binder clip. When a new tool is introduced, it will be a novelty. Anticipate that students will be curious and excited with the new items when first used, and as the novelty fades, students will carry on as usual, using the tool productively.

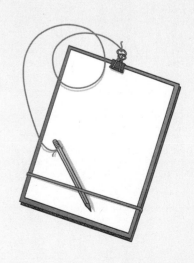

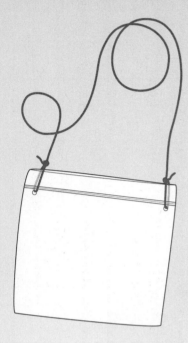

A group writing surface is important sometimes. You can use blue painter's tape to attach a sheet of chart paper temporarily to a wall or clip it onto a chain-link fence with binder clips or clothespins. On windy days, attach all four corners.

A small pack can serve as a hands-free means for students to tote their equipment. Little backpacks are excellent, but a serviceable low-cost satchel can be crafted from a large plastic zip bag and string. Purchase enough gallon-size zip bags for your class. Punch two holes just *under* the ends of the zipper. (This reduces tearing.) Cut the strings about 1 meter long. Tie sturdy knots that will not come undone. Store the string inside the bag after use to prevent tangling with other bags.

Hand lenses may disappear when students place them on the ground to perform a task. Run bright-colored string or yarn through holes in the lenses for students to wear. If your hand lenses do not already have holes, see if you can get holes drilled through the handles.

MANAGING STUDENTS

Going outdoors regularly is the best way to develop a productive and joyful working relationship with students in the outdoors. When students realize that going outdoors to learn is not a special event but, rather, a science event that will occur routinely, you may be surprised at how quickly they adapt to their expanded, enriched classroom.

Before the First Outing

It is always important to let the school administration know that you and your students will periodically be out of the classroom. If you are planning to leave the school grounds, remember to file a flight plan describing your itinerary, anticipated time of return, and contact partners.

At the beginning of the school year, send a letter home to families, letting them know that learning will extend to the schoolyard and, possibly, beyond. It may be possible to have a signed permission slip for impromptu walking field trips outside the schoolyard. Have families put their contact information and specific student health information on the permission slip. Photocopy these, and have one set of copies in the office and another set in a zip bag in your outdoor equipment bag for emergencies.

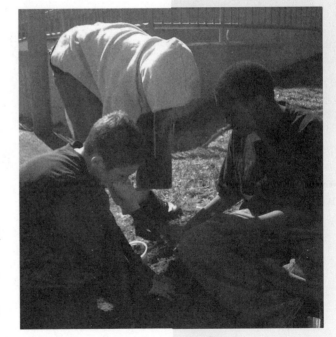

Tell students at the beginning of the year that they will be going outdoors often during science class. Remember to let them know a day in advance that they will be going outdoors. Let them know what it means to dress appropriately. This is especially important in the cold or stormy season when students will need proper clothing for safety and comfort. Your class can go out in any weather if students are dressed appropriately. A consistent system of reminders and clothing preparation will train students to be prepared.

Safety rules. Creating consistent, considerate rules of engagement is important. Learning is enhanced, and behavior problems are largely averted by establishing norms of outdoor study that students participate in developing and understand.

Have a discussion about what students think constitutes proper preparation and behavior for leaving the classroom to study outdoors.

(This discussion may be most productive *after* an initial orientation excursion to survey the schoolyard resources.) Have students generate a list of behaviors that they can adopt and respect. You may want to generate a second list of behaviors that you will agree to as leader of the adventure. Introduce as much formality into the process as you deem important. Develop the idea of a contract that all members of the class sign. Post the contract in your classroom and reference the *FOSS Outdoor Safety* poster. Here are the behaviors and rules that should appear on the list.

- Walk quickly and quietly outdoors.
- Outdoor science is not recess.
- Listen to the teacher's instructions.
- Freeze when the teacher rings the bell.
- Stay inside the boundaries.
- Don't make noise near the classrooms.
- Don't injure plants and animals in any way.
- Leave the outdoor environment the way you found it. Never release living organisms into the local environment unless they were found there.

TEACHING NOTE

Occasionally, a student may be uneasy working outdoors or feel it is not safe for a variety of reasons. Be sensitive to this, but know that with routine and regular outings, students will feel more comfortable, and outdoor behaviors will improve.

First Outing

Your first trip to the schoolyard may be a bit chaotic. Students may be distracted by other activities going on, and they may lapse into recess mode. A few precautions will minimize disruptive behaviors.

The path of egress. Determine which doors are available to access your outdoor site. Make sure you follow your school's policy for using auxiliary doors during the school day. Do they need to be closed at all times, or can you prop one open? Are they locked from the outside? You may be able to access keys in order to reduce travel time. When possible, avoid using the door you would normally use for recess. Students have a different mind-set when they walk onto the schoolyard through the "outdoor classroom" door.

Orientation activity. Consider an orientation activity for your first outing. The stated goal might be a site tour to inventory the resources on hand. Your primary agenda, however, is to dissipate the energy generated by the novelty of leaving the classroom during class time. Focus on preparing your transition to the outdoors, moving out in a purposeful and orderly fashion and arriving at your predetermined "home base," a destination that you will always go to initially when you leave the classroom. Form a sharing circle, a process you will use time and again. Tour the schoolyard, proceeding as a whole group, then ask students to walk as individuals for a few minutes, then with a partner for a minute, and finally with a group of four. This gives students a brief experience with each of the four ways they will be organized for various outdoor activities. End with another sharing circle and an orderly return to the classroom.

Challenging students. Sometimes the class will be inattentive or inappropriately rambunctious. At such times, it is appropriate to direct students back to the classroom. Breaking the contract has consequences, and students need to understand that the opportunity to learn in nature is a privilege. They will remember that day.

In rare instances, you may have an individual student who is regularly not able to comply. Interestingly, this is probably not the student who you anticipated would have difficulty. Often, students who have difficulty with attention and performance in traditional classroom seat work shine and take leadership outdoors. In the case of the noncompliant student, it may be necessary to ask him or her to take a time-out if he or she is able to sit without disrupting others' experiences. If the bad behavior persists, you may be obliged to return to the classroom early. Even so, it is important to give the student a chance to redeem himself or herself the next time you go outdoors.

Routines

Routines are good for management. They impose a measure of self-monitoring because they represent behaviors that are already known and have been practiced. If one person transgresses during a routine, other students are able to intervene to help you with student management. Here are a few routines that may work for you.

Science door. Have you ever watched a group of students pass through the exterior door on their way to recess? As soon as one foot hits the asphalt, they start running and cheering. It is a beautiful sight. Clearly, this is not how you want students to leave the building as you head out for science. One subtle but effective way to distinguish science from recess is to use a different door for science than for recess. Refer to this exit as the "learning door."

Transition behavior. Be explicit about how you want students to walk through the hallways and into the schoolyard. If students exit wildly, simply ring the bell, have them line up inside, and try it again. If this continues to be a problem, return to the classroom and try another day. By consistently showing students that this behavior limits their time outdoors, they usually adopt more compliant behavior.

Home base. Establish a destination in the schoolyard where every outdoor activity will begin. Students should walk directly there after leaving the school building. Choose a place that is level and, if possible, away from classroom windows and popular recess areas.

Sharing circle. When students arrive at home base, they should form a large sharing circle—everyone in a single ring with no students hanging back. This is an effective way to maintain eye contact with all students while you give instructions or share findings. Take a position in the circle where you are facing the Sun. This way, you will know that students won't be distracted by having the Sun's glare in their eyes. A sharing circle is also used to transition from one task to another, to summarize an activity, or anytime you need to regroup.

Techniques for forming a circle vary. One method is "magnetic feet." Students spread their legs to meet their neighbors' feet. Magically, these magnets turn off when you direct them to do so. Students may also stand with hands on hips, elbows touching with neighbors'. Pick or create a method that works with your students.

To speed up the formation of a sharing circle, try the tried-and-true countdown from five, with the objective that everyone is in a proper circle by zero.

Attention signal. Adopt a uniform signal for attention. It is essential that students respond to the attention signal immediately. You may choose the same method you use in the classroom or, if this is not appropriate for the outdoors, try one of these.

- A chime, bell, whistle, or other singular and loud sound. These are appropriate outdoors. When students hear it, they stop, look, and listen.

- Count down from five and when you get to one, students are silent with their hands up. This might not be appropriate outdoors. A countdown from ten can be used to call students back to a sharing circle.

- Clap call and response. You clap a pattern, and students return it by repeating the clapping pattern. This works if students are all nearby.

Focus question. Inquiry-based activities are guided by a question. This pedagogical routine should extend into the schoolyard, too. *Students need to know why they are engaged in the outdoor investigation.* They should expect to write the focus question in their notebooks at the outset of the investigation and produce an answer at the end of the investigation.

Boundaries. Setting boundaries allows students freedom within a defined space. Because different activities may require different locations, it is always important to be explicit about where students are allowed to travel during the outdoor activity.

Buddy system. You may want to institute a buddy system, particularly if you leave the schoolyard. When participants are paired off, tell them that each individual is responsible at all times for the whereabouts and safety of his or her buddy. It is helpful and fun to number the pairs in order to count off quickly and account for everyone.

Considerations for Students with Disabilities

FOSS evolved from pioneering work done in the 1970s with students with physical disabilities. The legacy of that work is that FOSS investigations incorporate multisensory methods, not only to accommodate students with physical and learning disabilities, but also to maximize information gathering for all students. Strategies that provide opportunities to learn for students with disabilities turn out to be good strategies for all students.

All students benefit from opportunities to experience the natural world outdoors. For students with disabilities, consider how to make the schoolyard accessible and safe so that they can work with a degree of independence. This requires advance planning to make sure that the student, his or her family, the special education teacher, and others involved in the child's school experience are informed and have input into the process.

Whenever a student with a disability is successful in a full-inclusion classroom, there is a behind-the-scenes collaborative effort of caring educators who work together to support the student with just the right amount of scaffolding. In advance of teaching the first outdoor activity, contact the special education teachers in charge of each student's Individualized Education Plan (IEP), and have them review the planned outdoor experiences. Ask the teachers to recommend modifications that will better accommodate and support each student. Invite the special educators to join the class for the outdoor activity.

Attention and language-based disabilities. Students with attention and behavioral issues often thrive when they are engaged in science outdoors. A fenced area will help you to both keep track of students and provide a sense of safety. Having students work with partners (buddies) allows students to look after each other. Provide short, structured opportunities for students to participate in outdoor activities in a clearly defined space, and expand the boundaries and time expectations as students earn your trust and confidence.

Consider students' communication requirements, and plan to bring specialty devices outdoors with you. This might be as simple as some picture cue cards to help enhance your message or an electronic communication device such as a computer or tablet.

Physical disabilities and visual impairments. In the Getting Ready section of each outdoor activity, we ask that the teacher decide where the outdoor activity should be taught. You may find that certain locations are better than others for the purposes of developing science concepts and meeting the physical needs of students with disabilities. Get to know your schoolyard really well, and try to experience it as your students do.

One side of most schoolyards is typically a parking lot, and the other three sides have spaces accessible to students for work and play. If you have a student with a physical disability, you need to consider if the terrain provides for good mobility for the student. Often, schoolyards are accessible because they are covered in asphalt. For many of the FOSS outdoor activities, an asphalt area is appropriate to use. When you want to use a greener location, make sure wheelchairs or crutches will work on these new surfaces. If the surface will be a mobility challenge, see if a paraprofessional or an educational assistant is able to help the student. If someone is not able to join you, consider if a classmate can help. If this is not an option, then consider working at a transition zone where the grass meets the asphalt.

A student with a visual impairment should make a scouting trip to the outdoor site with a mobility instructor to get the lay of the land and to learn where things are located. If the student becomes familiar with and knows how to navigate his or her outdoor surroundings, it will allow for more independence. Even so, during the actual outdoor activity, the student may need someone to quietly describe the terrain ahead and may need a fellow student's arm for balance and security.

If a student struggles with gross motor coordination, uneven ground may present a challenge. Just as you would in the classroom, begin by offering more support, and slowly pull back on this assistance as students become more comfortable with their stamina, security, and endurance with regular outdoor activities.

Sensory sensitivity. For a student with tactile-sensitivity issues, make it clear that he or she may, for example, observe as a classmate digs in the soil to collect a sample. Over time, this student may feel better able to participate by using gloves or by washing his or her hands as soon as the digging is complete. Knowing where each student falls on the continuum of a disability will help you decide when to hold back asking a student to fully participate, when to allow him or her to just observe, and when to give a gentle nudge and expect more active participation.

For students with sensory disorders, the outdoors is often a calming space. Consider where the quietest place in the schoolyard is, and use this more often if you have students with sensitivity to noise.

No matter what the disability, educators have found success taking students outdoors. With advance planning, communication with the student and the special education team, and a little extra effort, you, too, can provide a rich, safe outdoor learning experience for all your students.

TEACHING STRATEGIES

In the beginning, you may find that students regularly use descriptive terms such as "icky," "yucky," and "gross." You may have students who say things such as "I cannot get my clothes dirty. My mom will be mad." Many students are fearful of bugs, wooded areas, and even just sitting on the grass. Often, after a few outdoor activities, these fears and excuses fade away. With patience, persistence, and support, students' resistance may be overcome entirely. If you suspect that your students may be reluctant to work outdoors, structure your first few activities to be low-stress activities. The first few times outdoors can be fairly benign activities with students choosing a comfortable place to just sit

(or stand), practicing writing outdoors, and doing simple collecting or counting tasks.

Set the tone. Many teaching strategies that are effective in the classroom work outdoors, too. For example, at the sharing circle, instead of instinctively talking louder (because it is noisy outdoors), kneel down and speak in a loud whisper so that students need to focus to hear you. If students are speaking, put up your silent signal, and wait for silence. The educator's voice sets the tone for the activity.

Take a position. In the sharing circle, position yourself where you have the Sun in your face so that students don't need to squint. If possible, place yourself next to those students who might benefit from a silent look or hand on the shoulder to remind them to be silent.

Meet the challenge. Students who struggle with behavior problems often respond well outdoors when given responsibility. Let the active student carry the heavy jug of water or take the position at the front of the line to lead the class outdoors. For many students, this is all it takes to get them off on the right foot for the outdoor activity.

Students who have the greatest difficulty controlling their behavior indoors are often the leaders when it comes to working in an outdoor space. You may find that students who are not as attentive or cannot sit still inside are the most insistent about quieting down so that the class can get outdoors for science.

Get them writing. Primary students (grades K–2) can fill out a chart on a clipboard outdoors. They are also capable of recording observations outdoors in their notebooks if observation is their only task. Most primary students will need to sit down with their clipboards on their laps or on the ground to do this successfully. In the early years, most writing follows an outdoor activity and is done inside on desks and with the classroom's word wall.

Upper-elementary students (grades 3–6) are capable of writing outdoors. Students will benefit from a quick activity about how to place the notebook or clipboard in the crook of their nonwriting arm for support.

Depending on the activity, you might decide to have students attach their notebooks to a clipboard and place the clipboards in a crate for easy transport and storage. This technique is useful when the ground is moist, when the activity is messy, or when students need to use their hands to complete the activity. The recording will happen immediately after the hands-on activity. Be open to the surprise of how much your students are capable of noticing and recording during and after an outdoor activity.

FLOW OF OUTDOOR ACTIVITIES

The natural flow of a FOSS outdoor activity is slightly different from that of a standard FOSS indoor activity. The steps of a typical outdoor activity are listed below. This list may be helpful if you want to teach more than the handful of outdoor activities in the *Investigations Guide*, or if you want to adapt an indoor activity for schoolyard use.

1. **Prepare for the outdoor activity.**

   • Determine the best location to teach the activity.

   • Check the weather forecast.

   • Make sure students will be dressed appropriately.

   • Prepare materials for distribution.

   • Check the site the morning of the activity.

2. **Set the learning objective.**

   • Present the focus question.

   • Discuss procedures.

3. **Go outdoors.**

   • Gather at the predetermined location.

4. **Describe the activity.**

   • Organize students.

   • Define boundaries.

   • Introduce/distribute materials.

5. **Monitor the activity.**

   • Check student engagement.

   • Check student recording.

   • Ask questions.

6. **Share the experience.**

   • Form a sharing circle to discuss experiences.

   • Share thinking.

   • Share answers to the focus question.

7. **Return to class**

   • Make connections to the related indoor activity.

   • Display student work and collections.

EXTENDING BEYOND FOSS OUTDOOR ACTIVITIES

Occasionally, you may stumble upon a serendipitous opportunity. A breeze may launch thousands of twirling seeds from a maple tree, a woodpecker may alight on a tree so close that students can observe it drumming for insects, student-made parachutes may be carried by an updraft high into the sky and out of sight. To your delight, you may spy something you have never seen before. It can happen at any time when you are outdoors!

At special moments like these, our job as educators is to signal students to stop and quietly appreciate the suspension of time. Sometimes, words break the wonder. Trust your instincts at magical moments like these. The answers to questions will come eventually. It is not essential to label the event or even understand it. By inviting students to be alive with their feelings in the moment, you give them a gift for a lifetime.

It is not uncommon for educators to experience the powerful effect of the outdoors on student learning. If you find yourself searching for other outdoor learning opportunities, consider the ones below.

Move activities outdoors. Whatever the subject, students will have more room outdoors to be creative with some activities, and you can worry less about water, sand, and gravel spills. You must still consider how to transport materials, where students will sit, how they will return their project to the classroom, and how to clean up the outdoor space and students' hands before returning to the building.

Use the outdoors for extensions. Extending an inside concept to the outdoors is an excellent way to apply new knowledge. For example, in the **Structures of Life Module**, students grow bush beans hydroponically. If the large leaves fascinate students, go outdoors and see how many kinds of leaves you can find in the schoolyard. Do they all have smooth edges and come to a point at their tips? Go on a leaf hunt, group the leaves by their characteristics, and, eventually, have students tape them into their science notebooks.

There is great value in repeating an indoor activity outdoors. If your students are sanding wood samples inside, follow this up with a trip outdoors to find a stick and sand it. Have you been studying sow bugs? Ask students if they think they know where in the schoolyard they might find these bugs. Applying what students have learned in the classroom and putting that knowledge to work outdoors is an effective way to solidify their understanding. It's also an effective way to informally assess whether students understand the concepts, as well as a method for reinforcing the learning.

> **TEACHING NOTE**
>
> *Most states have an Environmental Literacy Plan, and some states, districts, or schools have a strong push for helping students become environmentally literate. Review the Interdisciplinary Extensions section at the end of each FOSS investigation for specific projects to develop students' environmental literacy.*

Find solitude. Use your outdoor space for silent independent work time. Just as in the classroom, the outdoor space can be a workspace with activities going on. At times, the outdoor space is more of a sanctuary for independent observation and notebook writing. It can be a place for special classroom rituals, awakening awareness of the beauty of nature. Sometimes, it can just be a place to be silent for a minute to awaken the senses and refocus students' energy. Some teachers increase this silent minute to 2, 3, or even 5 minutes. Silence is something to be practiced, and for many students and teachers, this can be challenging. This is a special way to end an outdoor experience and will help students transition into the classroom.

Enhance biodiversity. Modify your schoolyard by adding natural materials, such as logs, rocks, or paving stones. These structures can provide safe havens that may attract more living things. These types of shelters can be particularly helpful if you have an environment without natural shelter from the Sun, such as trees and shrubs. Students can also be involved in the design and implementation of these projects.

Schoolyard modification of this kind requires administrative participation and the support of the school custodian. Marking the area with educational signage can further benefit the enhanced site. If your schoolyard habitat needs your intervention to cultivate biodiversity, understand that it can take a couple of years to get established. Areas completely surrounded by blacktop or concrete can become filled with living things if provided with food, shelter, and water.

Attract wildlife. There are many responsible ways to attract wildlife to your class windows with feeders for birds, squirrels, hummingbirds, or butterflies, as well as many great programs for monitoring these animals. See FOSSweb for ideas for additional wildlife observation projects.

Establish long-term studies. The possibilities for long-term studies are endless, ranging from weather monitoring to seasonal population variation. It can be as simple as adopting an observation location and visiting it monthly to monitor various aspects of change over time. See FOSSweb for ideas for long-term projects.

Create gardens. Planting a garden in raised beds or improved soil is an ambitious option for increasing the biodiversity of your schoolyard. Consider carefully, especially with a vegetable garden, the timing of the school year. In most parts of the country, the time when plants require the most support is during summer vacation. Even if you can get a summer program involved, we suggest starting with indigenous plants that bloom or mature in spring and fall and require little maintenance. Contact neighborhood gardening groups for assistance and volunteers.

▶ **NOTE**
Remember not to release any classroom animals into schoolyard environments.

TEACHING NOTE

See FOSSweb Regional Resources for ideas on long-term projects and organizations that can provide assistance.

ELEMENTARY-LEVEL ENVIRONMENTAL EDUCATION

In the early 1990s, David Sobel noticed something poignant about children's perceptions of the environment. If a child had been introduced to environmental issues at school that were presented in the context of doom-and-gloom scenarios, the child expressed a heightened sense of anxiety and hopelessness, which Sobel calls ecophobia (Sobel 1996). The implications of his finding should raise a cautionary flag. Sobel is not suggesting that we abandon teaching about the environment in our elementary schools. He is proposing a different approach to environmental education that will bring our children into natural, healthy relationships with environmental issues.

Effective early environmental education should focus on local and ultralocal issues. What is happening in our schoolyards? What factors influence the communities of plants and animals in our neighborhoods? How do changing weather conditions affect the populations around our schools? How are our actions affecting the habitats in our schoolyards? What can we do to enhance natural systems at our schools? Elaborate rain forest projects provide little understanding and have negligible impact on students' connections to nature; researching and installing a butterfly garden or keeping an inventory of the birds in the schoolyard can be transformative. The children from Sobel's 1996 study could tell you how many species in the Amazon were going extinct each minute, but were unfamiliar with the most common plants in their schoolyard.

Time outdoors during the school day is beneficial for student learning. Students who are exposed to hands-on experiences in their local environment often become enthusiastic, self-motivated learners and, typically, academically outperform their peers who do not have these learning opportunities (Liebermann and Hoody 1998). Children are able to pay attention for longer periods of time outdoors on the same assignment and are more focused when they return to their indoor class work (Louv 2008).

Research has produced evidence that using the schoolyard is an effective way to enhance student learning. Texas A&M University, in conjunction with the Texas Education Agency, conducted a meta-analysis of the research in order to identify and rank effective instructional methods for science education and to define how best to improve student achievement. The highest-ranked teaching strategy was Enhanced Context Strategies, which included taking meaningful field trips and using the schoolyard for activities (Scott et al. 2005).

Students' attitudes toward learning are influenced by simple outdoor experiences. In one study (Shaw and Terrance 1981), students who experienced outdoor instruction reported that, in general, they enjoyed school more and felt more supported and trusted by their teacher than they had prior to the outdoor experiences. These pretest/posttest differences were more pronounced for students who had been identified as being "uninvolved" in the classroom activities. Also, this student perception was a lasting effect that carried over to the regular classroom activities weeks later.

Perhaps the most important benefit of incorporating the outdoors into the traditional school learning environment is that it offers opportunities for students to synthesize concepts and personal experience by applying what they have learned to a new environment.

FOSS outdoor activities will help you focus on age-appropriate environmental topics and enable you to create meaningful and personal connections between your students and their local environment. When students can openly explore the environment, they can create meaningful connections to their learning and establish positive relationships with nature. You'll be amazed by what students notice.

In 2010, Kevin Coyle of the National Wildlife Federation (NWF) reported that the average American child spends 7 hours and 38 minutes per day indoors using electronic media (almost 12 hours for children ages 11-14) while only having a few minutes of unstructured play time daily in an outdoor setting. These statistics are alarming. At FOSS, we truly hope, that getting students outdoors regularly to explore science concepts in their schoolyard or in a nearby outdoor setting will help foster a desire to shut off the TV or computer and to get outside to embrace the natural world on their own time.

Here's the good news. If you focus on inquiry and direct experience instead of problems, it takes remarkably little guidance for students to make positive, empowering, lifelong connections to nature. One insightful young man explained, "My video games have a pattern that is always the same, but nature is like a game that is different every time you play." As an educator, you can draw out that sense of wonder and curiosity for students while simultaneously helping them build a solid science foundation.

REFERENCES

Coyle, Kevin J. 2010. *Back to School: Back Outside! How Outdoor Education and Outdoor School Time Create High Performance Students.* Reston VA: National Wildlife Federation.

LaForce, Melanie and Liz Bancroft. 2013. *Science in the Schoolyard Evaluation.* Chicago, IL: Outlier Research and Evaluation CEMSE, University of Chicago.

Liebermann, G., and L. Hoody. 1998. *Closing the Achievement Gap: Using the Environment as an Integrated Context for Learning; Results of a National Study.* San Diego: State Education and Environment Roundtable.

Louv, R. 2008. *Last Child in the Woods: Saving Our Children from Nature-Deficit Disorder.* New York: Workman Publishing.

Scott, T. et al. 2005. *Texas Science Initiative Meta-Analysis of National Research Regarding Science Teaching.* Texas Education Agency.

Shaw, T. J., and J. M. Terrance. 1981. "Involved and Uninvolved Student Perceptions in Indoor and Outdoor School Settings." *Journal of Early Adolescence,* 1:135–146.

Sobel, D. 1996. *Beyond Ecophobia: Reclaiming the Heart in Nature Education.* Great Barrington, MA: Orion Society.

ACKNOWLEDGMENTS

The Taking FOSS Outdoors initiative got its start through a collaboration with the Boston Schoolyard Initiative (BSI). In 2004, BSI began developing an approach to teaching science that routinely takes students into the schoolyard to test, apply, and explore core science concepts and skills. As part of this project, BSI developed *Science in the Schoolyard Guide*s™ for 12 FOSS modules and a companion *Science in the Schoolyard*™ video. In partnership with the City of Boston, BSI designs and builds schoolyards that provide a rich environment for teaching, learning, and play. Many of the behavior management strategies listed here were gleaned from expert Boston Public School teachers. We thank each of them for their contributions to this initiative and hope they know that the ripples of their work extend far beyond the city limits of Boston, MA to reach students across the country and throughout the world.

For more information on BSI, *Science in the Schoolyard*, or BSI's *Outdoor Writer's Workshop*™ professional development program and materials, see www.schoolyards.org.

The video, *Science in the Schoolyard*™ can be viewed on FOSSweb in Teaching Tools, Taking FOSS Outdoors.

Science Notebook Masters

Object Materials

What are solid objects made of?

Object	Material
Cylinder	
Triangle	
Tube	
Cloth	
Stick	
Wire	
Screw	

FOSS Next Generation
© The Regents of the University of California
Can be duplicated for classroom or workshop use.

Object Materials

What are solid objects made of?

Object	Material
Cylinder	
Triangle	
Tube	
Cloth	
Stick	
Wire	
Screw	

FOSS Next Generation
© The Regents of the University of California
Can be duplicated for classroom or workshop use.

Solids and Liquids Module
Investigation 1: Solids
No. 1—Notebook Master

Properties of Solid Objects

Object \ Property	Cylinder	Triangle	Tube	Cloth	Stick	Wire	Screw
Round							
Pointy							
Flexible							
Rigid							
Soft							
Hard							
Transparent							

Solids and Liquids Module
Investigation 1: Solids
No. 2—Notebook Master

FOSS Next Generation
© The Regents of the University of California
Can be duplicated for classroom or workshop use.

Properties of Solid Objects

Object \ Property	Cylinder	Triangle	Tube	Cloth	Stick	Wire	Screw
Round							
Pointy							
Flexible							
Rigid							
Soft							
Hard							
Transparent							

Solids and Liquids Module
Investigation 1: Solids
No. 2—Notebook Master

FOSS Next Generation
© The Regents of the University of California
Can be duplicated for classroom or workshop use.

Object Grouping

Can two or more objects have the same property?

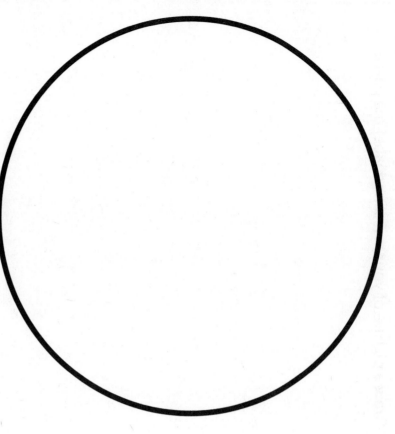

These objects share the property of

_____

Objects that have this property can be used for

_____
● _____

FOSS Next Generation
© The Regents of the University of California
Can be duplicated for classroom or workshop use.

Object Grouping

Can two or more objects have the same property?

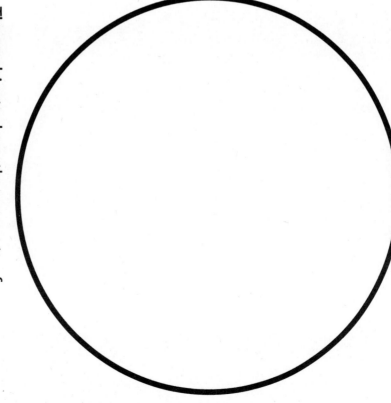

These objects share the property of

_____

Objects that have this property can be used for

_____
● _____

FOSS Next Generation
© The Regents of the University of California
Can be duplicated for classroom or workshop use.

Towers

What are the properties of successful towers?

a. Draw a picture of your tower and label the parts.

b. Write about the properties of the top of your tower.

c. Write about the properties of the base of your tower.

d. Write about one part of your tower that was very important to its success in the wind.

FOSS Next Generation
© The Regents of the University of California
Can be duplicated for classroom or workshop use.

Towers

What are the properties of successful towers?

a. Draw a picture of your tower and label the parts.

b. Write about the properties of the top of your tower.

c. Write about the properties of the base of your tower.

d. Write about one part of your tower that was very important to its success in the wind.

FOSS Next Generation
© The Regents of the University of California
Can be duplicated for classroom or workshop use.

Solids and Liquids Module
Investigation 1: Solids
No. 4—Notebook Master

Outdoor Solids

What solid objects are outdoors?

Object Property	Twig	Paper			
Smooth					
Rough					
Flat					

FOSS Next Generation
© The Regents of the University of California
Can be duplicated for classroom or workshop use.

Solids and Liquids Module
Investigation 1: Solids
No. 5—Notebook Master

Outdoor Solids

What solid objects are outdoors?

Object Property	Twig	Paper			
Smooth					
Rough					
Flat					

Liquid Exploration

How are liquids different from each other?

Some liquids are _____, but

other liquids are _____ .

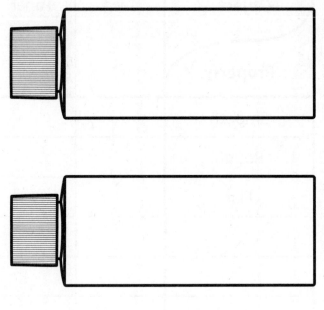

FOSS Next Generation
© The Regents of the University of California
Can be duplicated for classroom or workshop use.

Solids and Liquids Module
Investigation 2: Liquids
No. 6—Notebook Master

Liquid Exploration

How are liquids different from each other?

Some liquids are _____, but

other liquids are _____ .

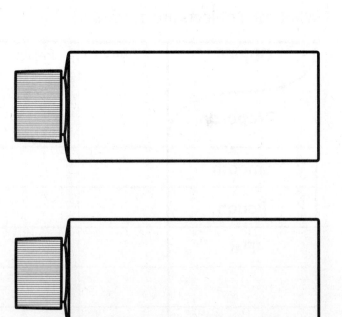

FOSS Next Generation
© The Regents of the University of California
Can be duplicated for classroom or workshop use.

Solids and Liquids Module
Investigation 2: Liquids
No. 6—Notebook Master

Liquid Properties

How can liquids be described?

Object Property	Water	Hand soap	Oil	Corn syrup	Water with color	Dish soap	Starch
Transparent							
Translucent							
Has color							
Viscous							
Bubbly							
Foamy							

Liquid Properties

How can liquids be described?

Object Property	Water	Hand soap	Oil	Corn syrup	Water with color	Dish soap	Starch
Transparent							
Translucent							
Has color							
Viscous							
Bubbly							
Foamy							

FOSS Next Generation
© The Regents of the University of California
Can be duplicated for classroom or workshop use.

Solids and Liquids Module
Investigation 2: Liquids
No. 7—Notebook Master

Liquids in Containers

1. Put one small vial of water in each container.

2. Draw the level of the water in each container.

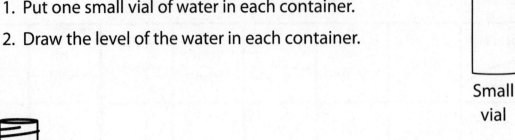

Small
vial

Solids and Liquids Module
Investigation 2: Liquids
No. 8—Notebook Master

FOSS Next Generation
© The Regents of the University of California
Can be duplicated for classroom or workshop use.

Liquids in Containers

1. Put one small vial of water in each container.

2. Draw the level of the water in each container.

Small
vial

Solids and Liquids Module
Investigation 2: Liquids
No. 8—Notebook Master

FOSS Next Generation
© The Regents of the University of California
Can be duplicated for classroom or workshop use.

Liquid Level in a Bottle

How does the liquid change when the bottle tips?

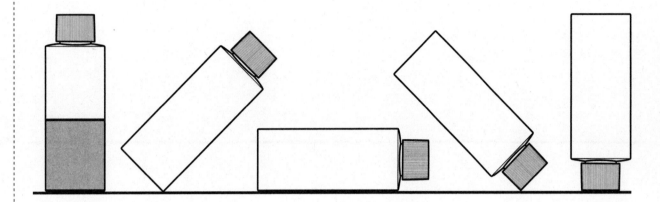

Draw what the liquid looks like in each picture
as the bottle turns upside down.

FOSS Next Generation
© The Regents of the University of California
Can be duplicated for classroom or workshop use.

Solids and Liquids Module
Investigation 2: Liquids
No. 9—Notebook Master

Liquid Level in a Bottle

How does the liquid change when the bottle tips?

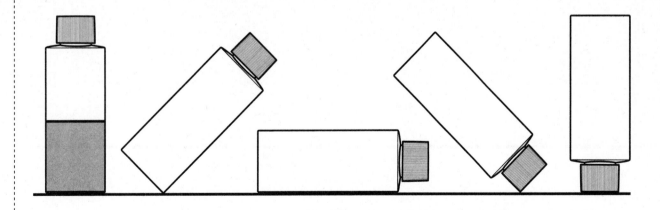

Draw what the liquid looks like in each picture
as the bottle turns upside down.

FOSS Next Generation
© The Regents of the University of California
Can be duplicated for classroom or workshop use.

Solids and Liquids Module
Investigation 2: Liquids
No. 9—Notebook Master

Falling-Bottle Puzzle

How do liquids change in containers?

_____

When liquids are in containers, the liquids _____

_____

_____

Solids and Liquids Module
Investigation 2: Liquids
No. 10—Notebook Master

FOSS Next Generation
© The Regents of the University of California
Can be duplicated for classroom or workshop use.

Falling-Bottle Puzzle

How do liquids change in containers?

_____

When liquids are in containers, the liquids _____

_____

_____

Solids and Liquids Module
Investigation 2: Liquids
No. 10—Notebook Master

FOSS Next Generation
© The Regents of the University of California
Can be duplicated for classroom or workshop use.

Soup Mix

How can mixtures of particles be separated?

Mixtures of particles can be separated by

_____

_____

_____

_____

_____

FOSS Next Generation
© The Regents of the University of California
Can be duplicated for classroom or workshop use.

Solids and Liquids Module
Investigation 3: Bits and Pieces
No. 11—Notebook Master

Soup Mix

How can mixtures of particles be separated?

Mixtures of particles can be separated by

_____

_____

_____

_____

_____

FOSS Next Generation
© The Regents of the University of California
Can be duplicated for classroom or workshop use.

Solids and Liquids Module
Investigation 3: Bits and Pieces
No. 11—Notebook Master

Bead Mix A

Which screens can separate beads?

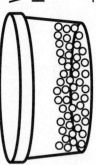

Which screens can these beads go through?

_____

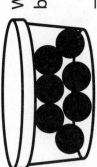

Which screens can these beads go through?

_____

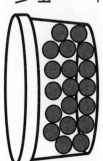

Which screens can these beads go through?

_____

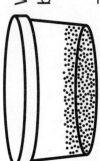

Which screens can these beads go through?

_____

FOSS Next Generation
© The Regents of the University of California
Can be duplicated for classroom or workshop use.

Bead Mix A

Which screens can separate beads?

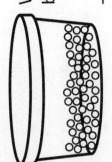

Which screens can these beads go through?

_____

Which screens can these beads go through?

_____

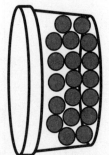

Which screens can these beads go through?

_____

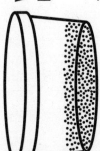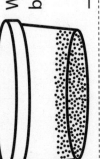

Which screens can these beads go through?

_____

Investigation 3: Bits and Pieces
Solids and Liquids Module
No. 12—Notebook Master

FOSS Next Generation
© The Regents of the University of California
Can be duplicated for classroom or workshop use.

Bead Mix B

Which screens can separate beads?

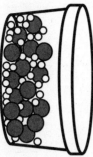

Which screens can separate
this mixture?
_____

Which screens can separate
this mixture?
_____

Which screens can separate
this mixture?
_____

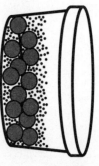

Which screens can separate
this mixture?
_____

Bead Mix B

Which screens can separate beads?

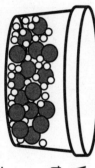

Which screens can separate
this mixture?
_____

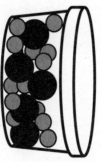

Which screens can separate
this mixture?
_____

Which screens can separate
this mixture?
_____

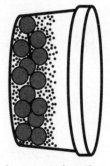

Which screens can separate
this mixture?
_____

Particles Outdoors

Are there little pieces of solid material outdoors?

We found _____ outdoors.

We poured _____ and water on the ground.
This is what we saw.

Water	Particles

FOSS Next Generation
© The Regents of the University of California
Can be duplicated for classroom or workshop use.

Solids and Liquids Module
Investigation 3: Bits and Pieces
No. 14—Notebook Master

Particles Outdoors

Are there little pieces of solid material outdoors?

We found _____ outdoors.

We poured _____ and water on the ground.
This is what we saw.

Water	Particles

FOSS Next Generation
© The Regents of the University of California
Can be duplicated for classroom or workshop use.

Solids and Liquids Module
Investigation 3: Bits and Pieces
No. 14—Notebook Master

FOSS Next Generation
© The Regents of the University of California
Can be duplicated for classroom or workshop use.

Solid Materials in Water A

What happens when solids are mixed with water?

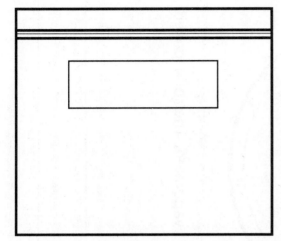

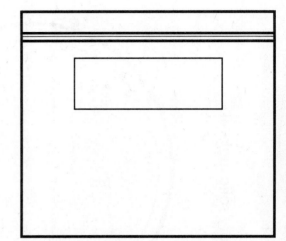

1. First, the solid was dry. The solid looked

_____

_____ .

2. After a night in water, the solid looked

_____

_____ .

Solids and Liquids Module
Investigation 4: Solids, Liquids, and Water
No. 15—Notebook Master

FOSS Next Generation
© The Regents of the University of California
Can be duplicated for classroom or workshop use.

Solid Materials in Water A

What happens when solids are mixed with water?

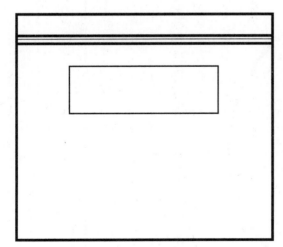

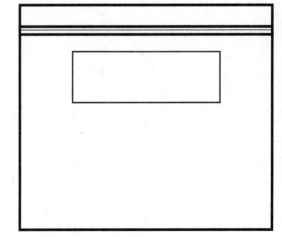

1. First, the solid was dry. The solid looked

_____

_____ .

2. After a night in water, the solid looked

_____

_____ .

Solids and Liquids Module
Investigation 4: Solids, Liquids, and Water
No. 15—Notebook Master

Solid Materials in Water B

Record what your dry solid looks like.

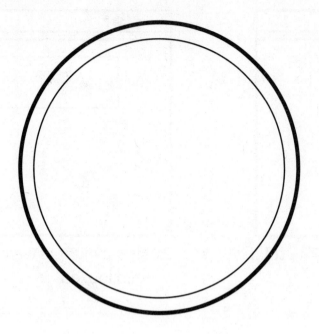

3. Then the water evaporated. The solid looked

_____

_____ .

FOSS Next Generation
© The Regents of the University of California
Can be duplicated for classroom or workshop use.

Solids and Liquids Module
Investigation 4: Solids, Liquids, and Water
No. 16—Notebook Master

Solid Materials in Water B

Record what your dry solid looks like.

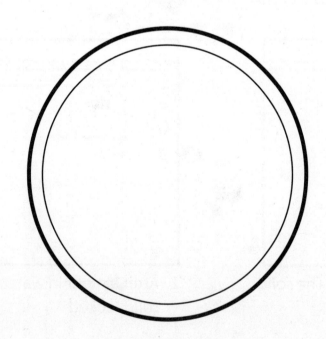

3. Then the water evaporated. The solid looked

_____

_____ .

FOSS Next Generation
© The Regents of the University of California
Can be duplicated for classroom or workshop use.

Solids and Liquids Module
Investigation 4: Solids, Liquids, and Water
No. 16—Notebook Master

Liquid with Water

What happens when _____ is mixed with water?

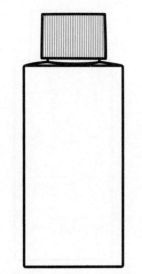 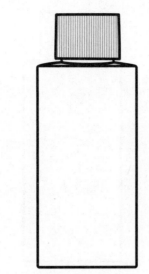 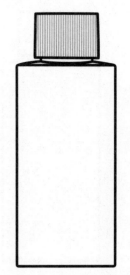

1. Add water. How does it look?

2. Shake it. How does it look?

3. How does it look the next day?

FOSS Next Generation
© The Regents of the University of California
Can be duplicated for classroom or workshop use.

Solids and Liquids Module
Investigation 4: Solids, Liquids, and Water
No. 17—Notebook Master

Liquid with Water

What happens when _____ is mixed with water?

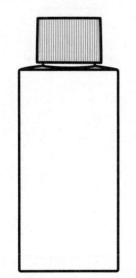  

1. Add water. How does it look?

2. Shake it. How does it look?

3. How does it look the next day?

FOSS Next Generation
© The Regents of the University of California
Can be duplicated for classroom or workshop use.

Solids and Liquids Module
Investigation 4: Solids, Liquids, and Water
No. 17—Notebook Master

Investigating Toothpaste

Is toothpaste solid or liquid?

 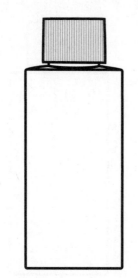 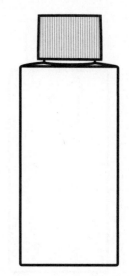

1. Add water. How does the toothpaste look?

_____

2. Shake it. How does the toothpaste look?

_____

3. After a day, how does the toothpaste look?

_____

FOSS Next Generation
© The Regents of the University of California
Can be duplicated for classroom or workshop use.

Solids and Liquids Module
Investigation 4: Solids, Liquids, and Water
No. 18—Notebook Master

Investigating Toothpaste

Is toothpaste solid or liquid?

1. Add water. How does the toothpaste look?

_____

2. Shake it. How does the toothpaste look?

_____

3. After a day, how does the toothpaste look?

_____

FOSS Next Generation
© The Regents of the University of California
Can be duplicated for classroom or workshop use.

Solids and Liquids Module
Investigation 4: Solids, Liquids, and Water
No. 18—Notebook Master

Changing Properties

How do properties of materials
change when they are heated or cooled?

When it gets ——————, a solid changes to
a liquid.

We say the solid ——————.

When it gets ——————, a liquid changes to
a solid.

We say the liquid ——————.

Changing Properties

How do properties of materials
change when they are heated or cooled?

When it gets ——————, a solid changes to
a liquid.

We say the solid ——————.

When it gets ——————, a liquid changes to
a solid.

We say the liquid ——————.

FOSS Next Generation   Solids and Liquids Module
© The Regents of the University of California   Investigation 4: Solids, Liquids, and Water
Can be duplicated for classroom or workshop use.   No. 19—Notebook Master

Teacher Masters

LETTER TO FAMILY

Cut here and glue onto school letterhead before making copies.

Science News

Dear Family,

Our class is beginning a scientific study of solids and liquids. We will observe the properties of many solids and liquids, comparing how solids and liquids are alike and how they are different; organize the results of our inquiries; and communicate both orally and in writing the things we discover. These processes (observing, communicating, comparing, and organizing) are the basic thinking processes students need at this age to develop a scientific understanding of the world around them.

Your child may ask you for help finding solids and liquids at home. You'll want to discuss and compare the different characteristics of those you find. (For example, how are salt and sugar alike? How are they different?) You may find yourself observing what happens when solids and liquids are put together. Making lemonade or salad dressing can provide interesting observations when solids and liquids are mixed. Watching an ice cube melt is a way to observe a solid change to a liquid.

We're looking forward to lots of fun and lots of learning as we explore a world full of solids and liquids! You can get more information on this module by going to www.FOSSweb.com.

Sincerely,

FOSS Next Generation
© The Regents of the University of California
Can be duplicated for classroom or workshop use.

Solids and Liquids Module
Investigation 1: Solids
No. 1—Teacher Master

FOCUS QUESTION 1

How can solid objects be described?

How can solid objects be described?

How can solid objects be described?

How can solid objects be described?

How can solid objects be described?

How can solid objects be described?

How can solid objects be described?

How can solid objects be described?

How can solid objects be described?

How can solid objects be described?

How can solid objects be described?

How can solid objects be described?

How can solid objects be described?

How can solid objects be described?

FOSS Next Generation
© The Regents of the University of California
Can be duplicated for classroom or workshop use.

Solids and Liquids Module
Investigation 1: Solids
No. 2—Teacher Master

GROUPING CIRCLE

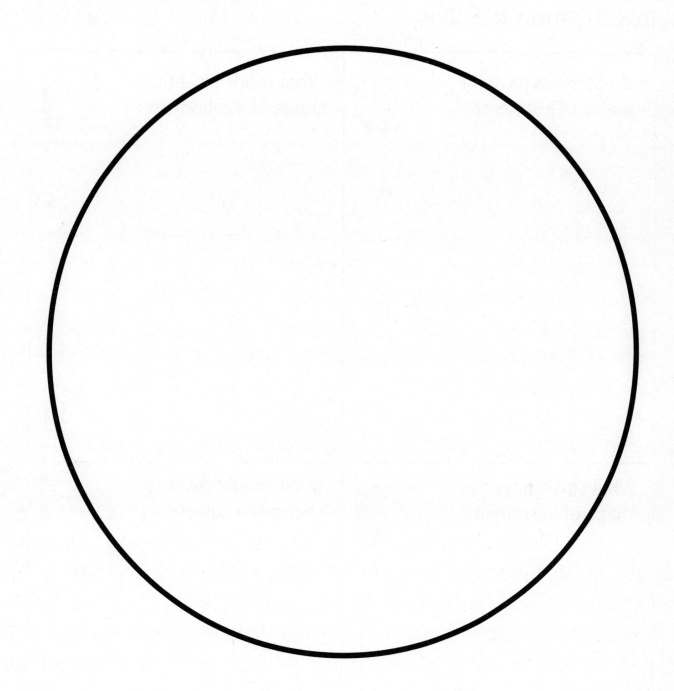

FOSS Next Generation
© The Regents of the University of California
Can be duplicated for classroom or workshop use.

Solids and Liquids Module
Investigation 1: Solids
No. 3—Teacher Master

Name _____   Date _____

MATH EXTENSION A
· ·
Investigation 1: Solids

What solids have the shape of a sphere?	What solids have the shape of a cylinder?
What solids have the shape of a pyramid?	What solids have the shape of a cube?

Name _____   Date _____

MATH EXTENSION B
· ·
Investigation 1: Solids

Cut out the boxes with the pictures of objects. Build towers with the pictures, using the clues your teacher gives you.

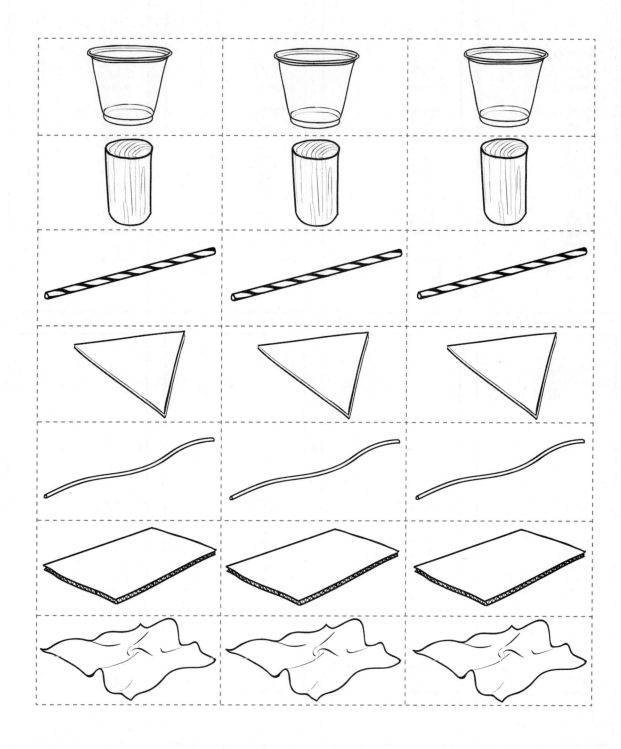

FOSS Next Generation
© The Regents of the University of California
Can be duplicated for classroom or workshop use.

Solids and Liquids Module
Investigation 1: Solids
No. 5—Teacher Master

MINI-SENTENCE STRIPS—SOLID

This solid is _____.

This solid is _____.

This solid is _____.

This solid is _____.

This solid is _____.

This solid is _____.

This solid is _____.

This solid is _____.

FOSS Next Generation
© The Regents of the University of California
Can be duplicated for classroom or workshop use.

Solids and Liquids Module
Investigation 1: Solids
No. 6—Teacher Master

HOME/SCHOOL CONNECTION

. . . .

Investigation 1: Solids

Play "I spy a solid object" with someone at home. These are some of the words we have been using in class to describe solids. Next to each word, draw or write the name of the solid you spied that matches the word. Add any other properties of solids that you spied.

I spy a solid object that is . . .	
flexible	rigid
smooth	rough
soft	transparent
flat	pointed

FOSS Next Generation
© The Regents of the University of California
Can be duplicated for classroom or workshop use.

Solids and Liquids Module
Investigation 1: Solids
No. 7—Teacher Master

MINI-SENTENCE STRIPS—LIQUID

This liquid is _____

This liquid is _____

This liquid is _____

This liquid is _____

This liquid is _____

This liquid is _____

This liquid is _____

This liquid is _____

FOSS Next Generation
© The Regents of the University of California
Can be duplicated for classroom or workshop use.

Solids and Liquids Module
Investigation 2: Liquids
No. 8—Teacher Master

CENTER INSTRUCTIONS—LIQUIDS IN BOTTLES

Materials

- 5   Basins
- 5   Sets of seven liquids
- 5   Large books or pieces of cardboard

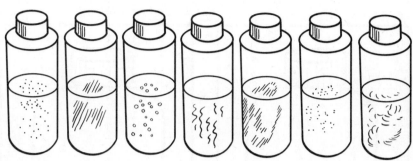

Set Up the Center

Space the five basins, each with seven bottles, evenly around the table.

Guide the Investigation

1. **Describe the investigation.** Show students a set of bottles. Tell students that their job is to work with a partner to find out as much as they can about the liquids in the bottles. Students are not allowed to open the bottles for any reason.

2. **Keep the activity moving forward.** Provide little guidance as students work with the bottles. Let students start a free exploration of the liquids.

3. **Focus the observations.** After students have worked with the bottles for several minutes, ask some guiding questions.

   - *How are the liquids the same? How are they different?*
   - *Do all the liquids move the same?*
   - *What happens to the liquids when you slowly tip the bottles on their sides? When you turn the bottles upside down?*
   - *What happens to the liquids when you spin the bottles?*
   - *What happens to the liquids when you roll the bottles across a flat table or down a ramp? Which bottles roll best?*
   - *What happens to the liquids when you shake the bottles?*
   - *Can you make a tornado in the bottles? In which ones?*

   If students focus on the identities of the liquids, ask them how the liquids are the same and how they are different. Emphasize their properties, but don't identify the liquids.

4. **Rotate groups.** After 20 minutes, ask students to return the bottles to the basins, and rotate the next group into the center.

FOSS Next Generation
© The Regents of the University of California
Can be duplicated for classroom or workshop use.

Solids and Liquids Module
Investigation 2: Liquids
No. 9—Teacher Master

MASTERS FOR CARD DECKS

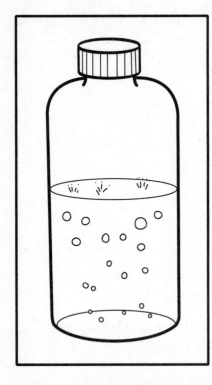

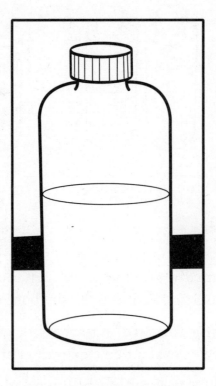

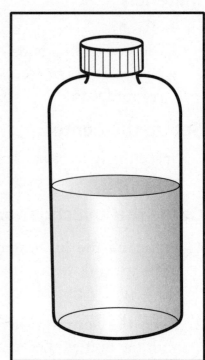

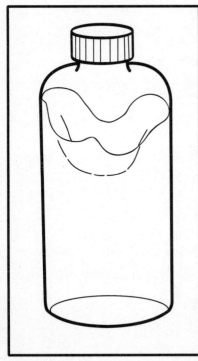

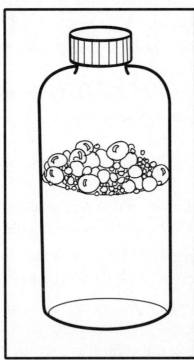

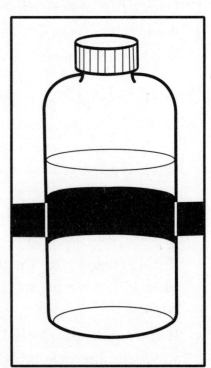

MEMORY TALLY

bubbly	viscous	foamy
translucent	has color	transparent

FOSS Next Generation
© The Regents of the University of California
Can be duplicated for classroom or workshop use.

Solids and Liquids Module
Investigation 2: Liquids
No. 11—Teacher Master

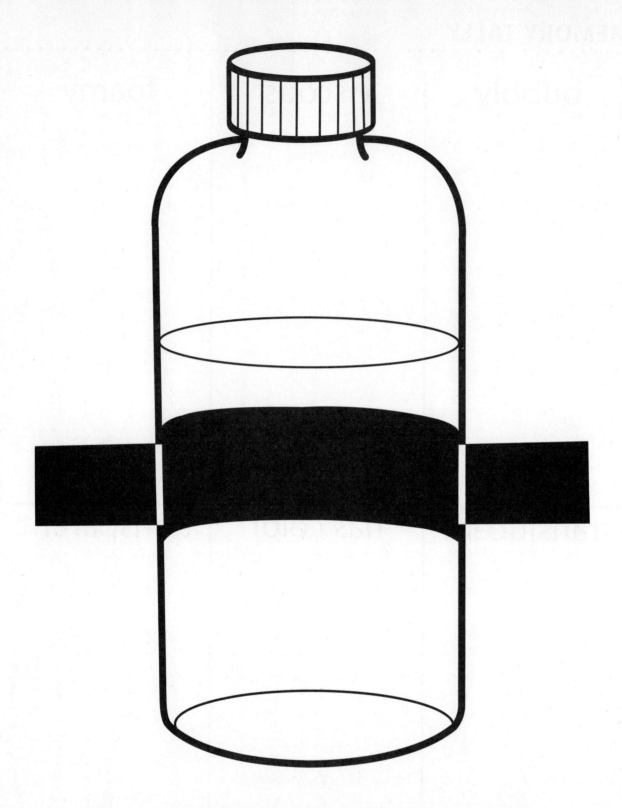

transparent

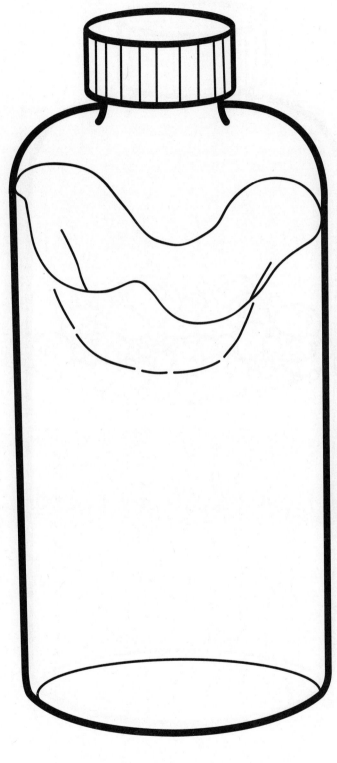

viscous

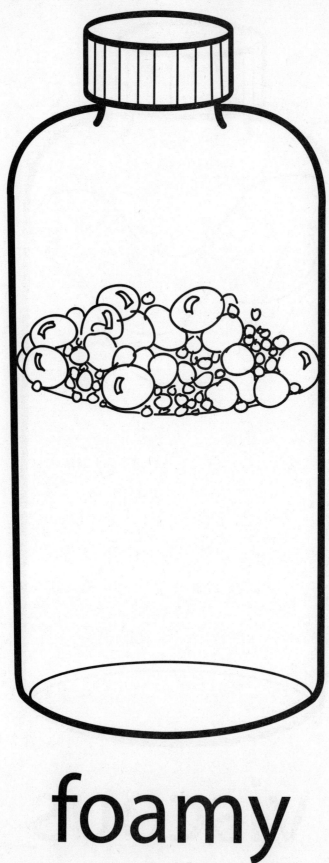

foamy

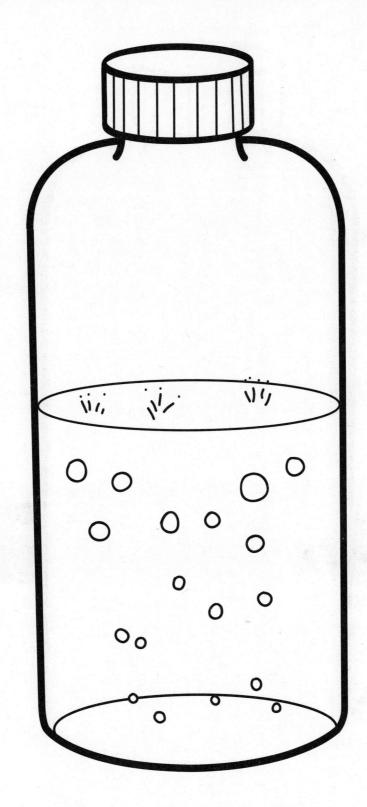

bubbly

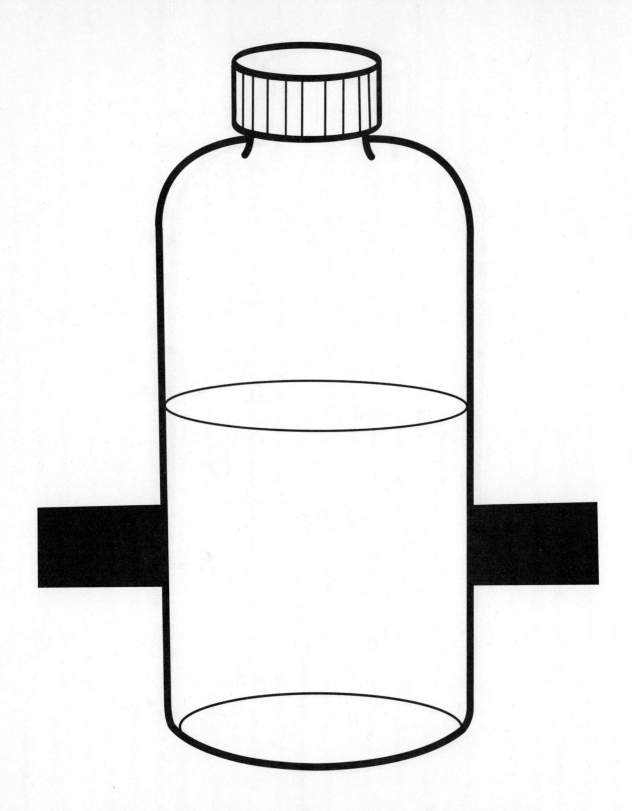

translucent

has color

CENTER INSTRUCTIONS—LIQUIDS IN CONTAINERS

Materials

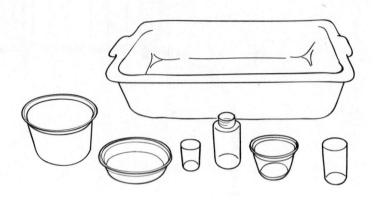

  5 Bus trays, each containing
       1 Container of water, 1 L
       1 Vial, 7 dram
       1 Vial, 12 dram
       1 Plastic bottle
       1 Container, 1/4 L
       1 Plastic cup
    Colored pencils or crayons
    Paper towels

Set Up the Center

Fill five 1-liter (L) containers with water. Add a drop of food coloring to each container. Space the five bus trays with their containers evenly around the table.

Have paper towels and colored pencils or crayons on hand.

Have a copy of notebook sheet 8, *Liquids in Containers*, for each student.

Guide the Investigation

1. **Introduce the investigation.** Show students a set of containers and the *Liquids in Containers* sheet. Describe the procedure, modeling the actions as you proceed.

   a. Work with a partner to line up the containers as they are on the sheet.
   b. Pour one full, *small* vial of water into each container.
   c. Draw a line on each picture showing the level of the water.
   d. Color the picture if you would like to.

2. **Suggest close observations.** As students work, ask,

   - *What is the shape of the water in the bottle? In the flat container? In the large vial? In the cup?*
   - *Which container looks like it has the most water in it?*
   - *Does each container have the same amount of water in it?*
   - *Where do you think the water level will be if we add another vial of water to each container?*

   Students can put a second vial of water into each container and draw a second line on each picture.

3. **Prepare the center for the next group.** When time is nearly up, ask students to pour all the water back into the 1 L container. Use the paper towels to clean up any spills. Make sure each bus tray has a complete set of containers.

FOSS Next Generation
© The Regents of the University of California
Can be duplicated for classroom or workshop use.

Solids and Liquids Module
Investigation 2: Liquids
No. 18—Teacher Master

FALLING-BOTTLE PUZZLE

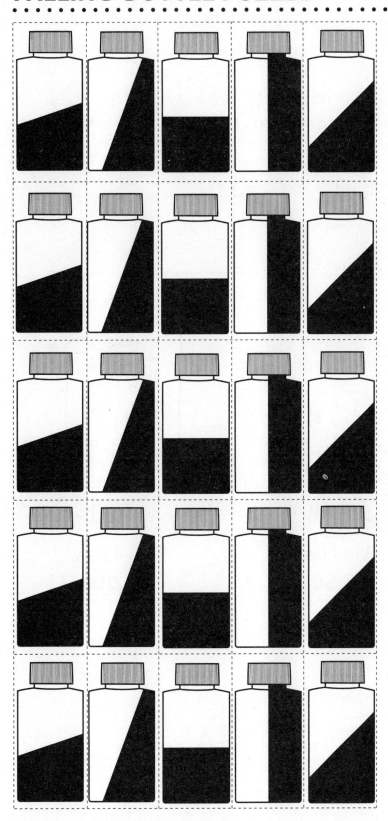

FOSS Next Generation
© The Regents of the University of California
Can be duplicated for classroom or workshop use.

Solids and Liquids Module
Investigation 2: Liquids
No. 19—Teacher Master

Name _____   Date _____

MATH EXTENSION
. . . .
Investigation 2: Liquids

A student went to the store with his mother to get a few things. They bought dish soap, milk, bran flakes, cheese, and bananas. The prices are listed below.

How much did they spend for liquids?   _____

How much did they spend for solids?   _____

Dish soap
$1.50

Bananas
$1.50

Bran flakes
$3.00

Milk
$2.00

Cheese
$2.50

FOSS Next Generation
© The Regents of the University of California
Can be duplicated for classroom or workshop use.

Solids and Liquids Module
Investigation 2: Liquids
No. 20—Teacher Master

HOME/SCHOOL CONNECTION

Investigation 2: Liquids

Find a container of liquid at home.
Draw a picture of the liquid.

Record the properties of the liquid.

This liquid is called _____.

This liquid has these properties.	Draw the bottle here.
☐ transparent	
☐ translucent	
☐ bubbly	
☐ viscous	
☐ foamy	
☐ has color	
☐ _____	
☐ _____	
☐ _____	

FOSS Next Generation
© The Regents of the University of California
Can be duplicated for classroom or workshop use.

Solids and Liquids Module
Investigation 2: Liquids
No. 21—Teacher Master

CENTER INSTRUCTIONS—SOLIDS IN CONTAINERS

Materials

- 5 Bus trays, each containing
  - 2 Plastic cups
  - 2 Bottles with caps
  - 2 Vials with caps, 12 dram
  - 2 Vials with caps, 7 dram
  - 1 Beaker
  - 1 Funnel
  - 1 Scoop
  - 1 Container of particles (cornmeal, rice, mung beans, pinto beans, or lima beans)
- 5 Wood cylinders
- 5 Screws

Set Up the Center

The cylinders and screws should be in a container in a central spot. Space the five bus trays with their containers and particles of solid material evenly around the table.

Guide the Investigation

1. **Describe the challenge.** Tell students that they will work with a partner to find out as much as they can about each of the five solid materials by transferring them from one container to another.

2. **Keep the activity moving forward.** Provide very little guidance as students work with the materials and containers. If necessary, remind students to work in the bus trays. Don't allow students to mix materials.

3. **Focus the observations.** Ask questions to focus students' observations on the properties of the solid materials.

   - *Put one level scoop of material in each container. Note the level of the material in each container. Does the highest level mean the most material?*
   - *Describe how these materials pour.*
   - *Can you put the material in a pile, a line, a circle, a square?*
   - *What happens when you put the wood cylinder and the screw in a cup of the material?*

4. **Move to a new station.** After students become familiar with the first material, suggest that they move to a new station to investigate a different material. Have students spend 3–5 minutes at each station.

FOSS Next Generation
© The Regents of the University of California
Can be duplicated for classroom or workshop use.

Solids and Liquids Module
Investigation 3: Bits and Pieces
No. 22—Teacher Master

CENTER INSTRUCTIONS—SEPARATING SOUP MIX

Materials

5 Bus trays, each containing
  - 1 Container of soup mix
  - 4 Containers, 1/2 L
  - 1 Scoop
  - 1 Screen, small mesh
  - 1 Screen, medium mesh
  - 1 Screen, large mesh

Set Up the Center

Space the five bus trays with their containers, scoop, screens, and soup mix evenly around the table.

Guide the Investigation

1. **Describe separating soup mix.** Tell students to work with a partner to separate the soup mix into containers in order to find out how many kinds of material are in the mixture.

2. **Keep the activity moving forward.** Provide very little guidance as students work with the soup mix and screens. If necessary, remind students to work in the bus trays. If they don't use the screens at the start, that's OK.

3. **Monitor the separation.** If, after an extended period of time, the screens are not being used, suggest that the screens might be useful. Ask,

   - *How are screens used?*
   - *Can screens be used to separate the soup mix?*
   - *Which screen is the best for separating cornmeal from the soup mix?*
   - *Can you get each of the materials in its own container?*

4. **Discuss separations.** After students have had some success separating the soup mix, ask some questions to focus students' thinking on the separation process.

   - *How many different materials were in the soup mix?*
   - *Were you able to separate the mix? How did you do it?*
   - *If you used the screens to sift the mixture, what is the best way to use them? Which screen did you use first?*

5. **Prepare the center for the next group.** When time is nearly up, ask students to return the soup mix to its original container. Make sure each bus tray has a complete set of screens and 1/2 L containers.

FOSS Next Generation
© The Regents of the University of California
Can be duplicated for classroom or workshop use.

Solids and Liquids Module
Investigation 3: Bits and Pieces
No. 23—Teacher Master

CENTER INSTRUCTIONS—SOLIDS IN BOTTLES

Materials

5   Bus trays, each containing
    4   Bottles with caps
    1   Scoop
    1   Funnel
    1   Container of cornmeal
    1   Container of rice
    1   Container of mung beans
    1   Container of lima beans
5   Large books or pieces of cardboard

Set Up the Center

Space the five bus trays with four bottles, four containers of solids, a funnel, and a scoop evenly around the table.

Guide the Investigation

1. **Describe filling the bottles.** Tell students that with a partner, they will fill bottles at one of the bus trays. Point out the funnel that students can use to direct the materials into the bottles.

    a. *Put the material from one container into one of the bottles. Put the cap on tightly.*
    b. *Repeat the process until a different material is in each bottle.*
    c. *Roll, shake, and tip the bottles while observing what happens.*

2. **Keep the activity moving forward.** Watch to see that students put only one kind of material in each bottle. Once the bottles are filled and the caps are screwed on tightly, provide very little guidance as students start their investigation.

    SAFETY NOTE: Caution students not to drop the bottles or hit them on anything, as they will crack. They should be handled carefully throughout the investigation.

3. **Suggest close observation of the bottles.** After students have had plenty of time to try their own ideas, ask questions to focus their observations.

    - *What happens when you turn the bottles upside down slowly?*
    - *What happens when you shake the bottles?*
    - *What happens when you spin the bottles on the floor?*
    - *What happens when you roll the bottles down a ramp and across the floor?*

4. **Prepare the center for the next group.** When time is nearly up, ask students to return the materials to their original containers. Make sure each bus tray has a complete set of bottles and materials.

FOSS Next Generation
© The Regents of the University of California
Can be duplicated for classroom or workshop use.

Solids and Liquids Module
Investigation 3: Bits and Pieces
No. 24—Teacher Master

SCREENS

1

1

2

2

3

3

FOSS Next Generation
© The Regents of the University of California
Can be duplicated for classroom or workshop use.

Solids and Liquids Module
Investigation 3: Bits and Pieces
No. 25—Teacher Master

Name _____   Date _____

MATH EXTENSION A
· ·
Investigation 3: Bits and Pieces

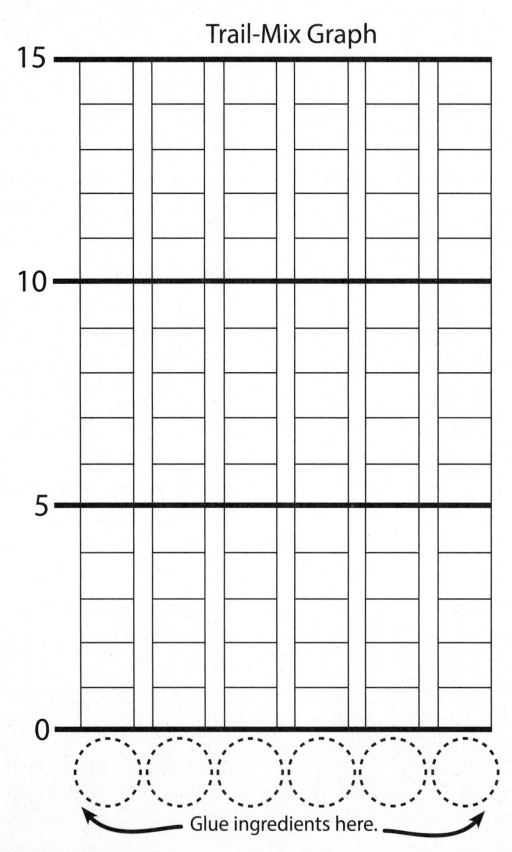

Trail-Mix Graph

FOSS Next Generation
© The Regents of the University of California
Can be duplicated for classroom or workshop use.

Solids and Liquids Module
Investigation 3: Bits and Pieces
No. 26—Teacher Master

Name _____   Date _____

MATH EXTENSION B

Investigation 3: Bits and Pieces

How many pinto beans can you grab
in one hand? Do it to find out, and
record the number here. _____

Will you be able to grab more, fewer, or the same number of lima
beans? (Circle one.)

More   Fewer   Same number

Why do you think so?

_____

_____

_____

_____

How many lima beans can you grab in
one hand? Do it to find out, and record
the number here. _____

FOSS Next Generation
© The Regents of the University of California
Can be duplicated for classroom or workshop use.

Solids and Liquids Module
Investigation 3: Bits and Pieces
No. 27—Teacher Master

HOME/SCHOOL CONNECTION

Investigation 3: Bits and Pieces

Soak, Slide, or Pile Up?

Compare what happens when you drop a spoonful of different materials on a paper towel. You might try water, rice, milk, flour, cornmeal, or dry beans. Then try the same materials on a different surface, such as plastic wrap or foil.

What did you observe?

Material	Solid or liquid	On paper towel	On other surface
Water			
Rice			

FOSS Next Generation
© The Regents of the University of California
Can be duplicated for classroom or workshop use.

Solids and Liquids Module
Investigation 3: Bits and Pieces
No. 28—Teacher Master

LABELS FOR SOLIDS IN WATER

Cookie Name _____	**Craft Stick** Name _____
Beans Name _____	**Cardboard** Name _____
Rice Name _____	**Mint** Name _____
Cloth Name _____	**Rock Salt** Name _____
Raisins Name _____	**Aluminum Foil** Name _____
Chalk Name _____	 Name _____

FOSS Next Generation
© The Regents of the University of California
Can be duplicated for classroom or workshop use.

Solids and Liquids Module
Investigation 4: Solids, Liquids, and Water
No. 29—Teacher Master

Name _____   Date _____

MATH EXTENSION A

Investigation 4: Solids, Liquids, and Water

1. What time is it when you start?

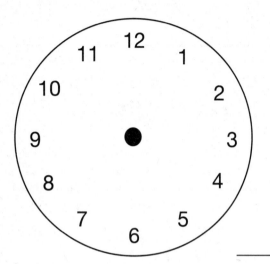

This is ice before it melted.

_____

2. What time is it when the ice is melted?

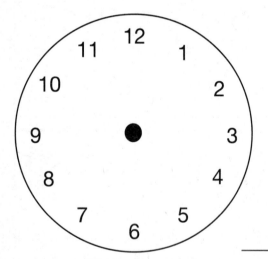

This is ice after it melted.

_____

3. How long did it take for the ice to melt?   _____

FOSS Next Generation
© The Regents of the University of California
Can be duplicated for classroom or workshop use.

Solids and Liquids Module
Investigation 4: Solids, Liquids, and Water
No. 30—Teacher Master

Name _____   Date _____

MATH EXTENSION B
· ·
Investigation 4: Solids, Liquids, and Water

A student made a new kind of soft drink. She tested many ways to put the solids and liquids together. Here is what she thought made the best-tasting soft drink.

Water	2 ounces
Sugar	4 spoons
Flavoring	3 spoons of vanilla, 2 spoons of strawberry
Coloring	5 drops of blue, 3 drops of red

Now she wants to make an 8-ounce portion of the soft drink that tastes just like her 2-ounce test. How much of each solid and liquid should she use?

FOSS Next Generation
© The Regents of the University of California
Can be duplicated for classroom or workshop use.

Solids and Liquids Module
Investigation 4: Solids, Liquids, and Water
No. 31—Teacher Master

HOME/SCHOOL CONNECTION

Investigation 4: Solids, Liquids, and Water

Salad Dressing

Cooks are chemists! Cooks investigate solids, liquids, and mixtures all the time. Make some tasty salad dressing to investigate what happens when solids and liquids are mixed.

You will need a plastic container with a lid, salt, oil, pepper, vinegar, and a spice such as rosemary, oregano, or basil.

1. Add 1/3 cup of vinegar to 1/2 cup of oil. Draw your observations.

2. Put on the lid and shake. Draw your observations.

3. Let it sit for 5 minutes. Draw your observations.

4. Add 1/2 teaspoon of salt and shake. What happens?	5. Add 1/4 teaspoon of pepper and shake. What happens?	6. Add _____ teaspoon of _____ and shake. What happens?

Try your salad dressing on a salad. How does it taste?

FOSS Next Generation
© The Regents of the University of California
Can be duplicated for classroom or workshop use.

Solids and Liquids Module
Investigation 4: Solids, Liquids, and Water
No. 32—Teacher Master

Assessment Masters

Embedded Assessment Notes

Investigation _____, Part _____   Date _____

Got it!

Concept

Concept

Reflections/Next Steps

Investigation _____, Part _____   Date _____

Got it!

Concept

Concept

Reflections/Next Steps

FOSS Next Generation
© The Regents of the University of California
Can be duplicated for classroom or workshop use.

Solids and Liquids Module
Embedded Assessment Notes
No. 1—Assessment Master

Performance Assessment Checklist—Solids and Liquids

Start date _____

End date _____

| Student names | Investigation 1, Part 3 | | |
	Planning and carrying out investigations	Constructing explanations	PS1. A: Structure and properties of matter	Patterns

FOSS Next Generation
© The Regents of the University of California
Can be duplicated for classroom or workshop use.

Solids and Liquids Module
Performance Assessment Checklist
No. 2—Assessment Master

Performance Assessment Checklist—Solids and Liquids

Start date _____

End date _____

Student names	Investigation 1, Part 4			
	Constructing explanations and designing solutions	ETS1.A: Defining and delimiting engineering problems	ETS1.B: Developing possible solutions	ETS1.C: Optimizing the design solution	Structure and function

FOSS Next Generation
© The Regents of the University of California
Can be duplicated for classroom or workshop use.

Performance Assessment Checklist—Solids and Liquids

Start date _____

End date _____

Student names	Investigation 2, Part 1			
	Planning and carrying out investigations	Obtaining, evaluating, and communicating information	PS1.A: Structure and properties of matter	Patterns

FOSS Next Generation
© The Regents of the University of California
Can be duplicated for classroom or workshop use.

Solids and Liquids Module
Performance Assessment Checklist
No. 4—Assessment Master

Performance Assessment Checklist—Solids and Liquids

Start date _____

End date _____

Student names	Investigation 3, Part 2		
	Planning and carrying out investigations	Constructing explanations	PS1.A: Structure and properties of matter	Scale, proportion, and quantity

Performance Assessment Checklist—Solids and Liquids

Start date _____

End date _____

| Student names | Investigation 3, Part 3 | | |
	Constructing explanations	PS1.A: Structure and properties of matter	Patterns

FOSS Next Generation
© The Regents of the University of California
Can be duplicated for classroom or workshop use.

Performance Assessment Checklist—Solids and Liquids

Start date _____

End date _____

Student names	Investigation 4, Part 3				
	Planning and carrying out investigations	Constructing explanations	Engaging in argument from evidence	Obtaining, evaluating, and communicating information	PS1.A: Structure and properties of matter	Cause and effect

Assessment Record—Investigation 1 and 2 I-Checks

Date _____

Student names	Investigation 1					Investigation 2			
	1	2	3	4	5	1	2	3	4

FOSS Next Generation
© The Regents of the University of California
Can be duplicated for classroom or workshop use.

Solids and Liquids Module
Performance Assessment Checklist
No. 8—Assessment Master

Assessment Record—Investigation 3 and 4 I-Checks

Date _____

Student names	Investigation 3				Investigation 4			
	1	2	3	4	1	2	3	4

FOSS Next Generation
© The Regents of the University of California
Can be duplicated for classroom or workshop use.

Solids and Liquids Module
Performance Assessment Checklist
No. 9—Assessment Master

INVESTIGATION 1 I-CHECK
SOLIDS AND LIQUIDS

1. Write **R** in the box if the object is **rigid**.

    Write **F** in the box if the object is **flexible**.

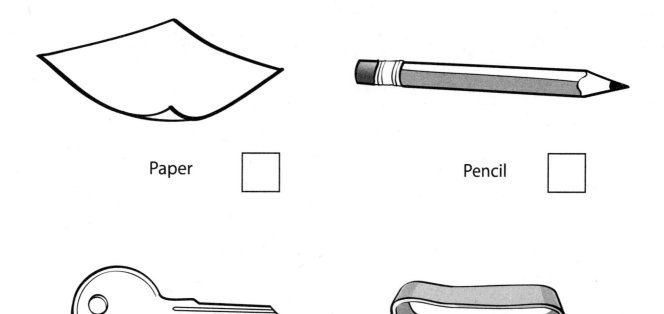

Paper ☐

Pencil ☐

Key ☐

Rubber band ☐

2. Look at the pencil your teacher is showing you.

    Label the picture below to show the **materials** the pencil is made of.

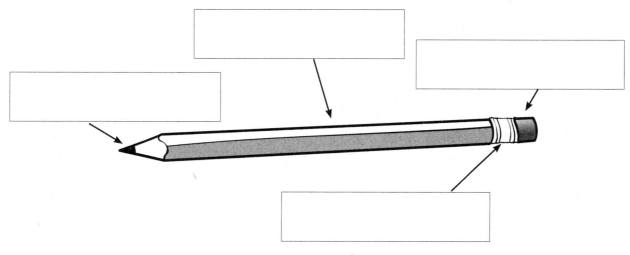

FOSS Next Generation
© The Regents of the University of California
Can be duplicated for classroom or workshop use.

Solids and Liquids Module
Investigation 1 I-Check
Page 1

INVESTIGATION 1 I-CHECK
SOLIDS AND LIQUIDS

• •

3.   You want to build the **tallest**, most **stable** tower you can with the objects shown below. Circle the objects you will use.

Will you use the **feather** or the **plastic cup** for the top of the tower?

Will you use the **piece of paper** or the **cardboard tube** for the middle of the tower?

Will you use the **ceramic mug** or the **air-filled beach ball** for the bottom of the tower?

 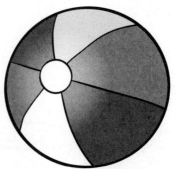

FOSS Next Generation
© The Regents of the University of California
Can be duplicated for classroom or workshop use.

Solids and Liquids Module
Investigation 1 I-Check
Page 2

INVESTIGATION 1 I-CHECK
SOLIDS AND LIQUIDS

4. A student used blocks to make the tower you see in the picture. Draw a new picture in the blank space. Show how the blocks could be taken apart and made into a new structure.

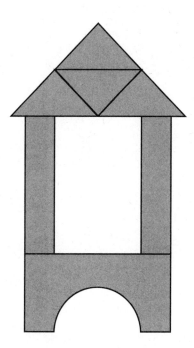

5. Write X next to the property word that can be used to describe all three objects.

  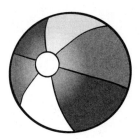

_____ straight

_____ rigid

_____ curved

_____ rough

FOSS Next Generation
© The Regents of the University of California
Can be duplicated for classroom or workshop use.

Solids and Liquids Module
Investigation 1 I-Check
Page 3

INVESTIGATION 2 I-CHECK
SOLIDS AND LIQUIDS

1. Draw a line from the property word to the picture of the liquid.

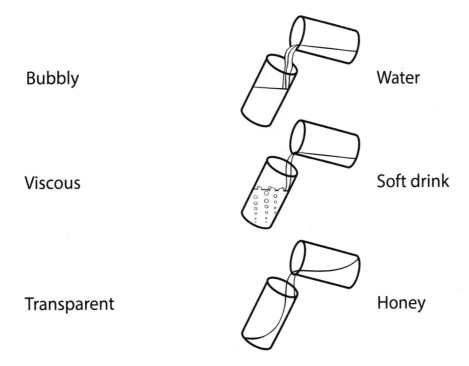

Bubbly

Viscous

Transparent

Water

Soft drink

Honey

2. There is a cup of liquid next to two empty containers. If you pour the liquid into the empty containers, what will they look like? Draw a line to show the liquid level.

Cup of liquid   New container 1   Cup of liquid   New container 2

FOSS Next Generation
© The Regents of the University of California
Can be duplicated for classroom or workshop use.

Solids and Liquids Module
Investigation 2 I-Check
Page 1

INVESTIGATION 2 I-CHECK
SOLIDS AND LIQUIDS

· ·

3. This is a drawing of a goldfish aquarium.

   Label the **solids** with an **S**.

   Label the **liquids** with an **L**.

   Label the **gases** with a **G**.

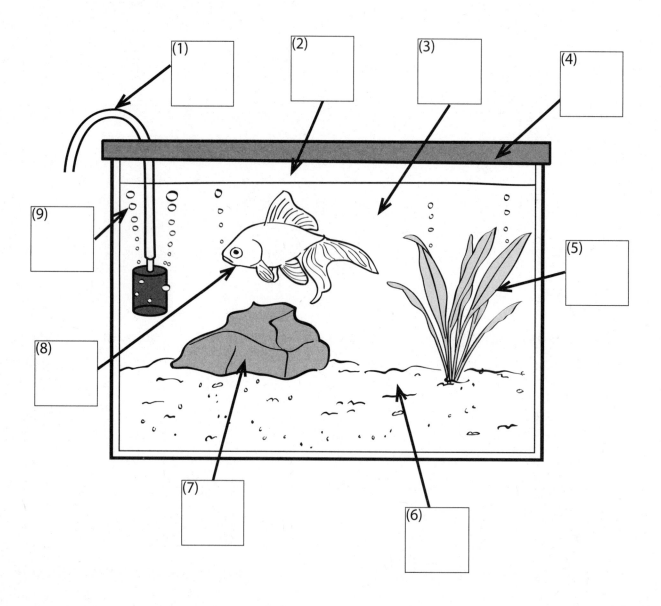

FOSS Next Generation
© The Regents of the University of California
Can be duplicated for classroom or workshop use.

Solids and Liquids Module
Investigation 2 I-Check
Page 2

INVESTIGATION 2 I-CHECK
SOLIDS AND LIQUIDS

4. The picture on the left shows a container with water in it.
   Draw the water in the bottles on the right to show what it looks like when the container moves.

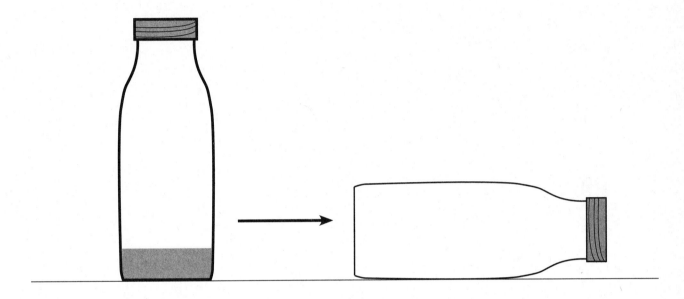

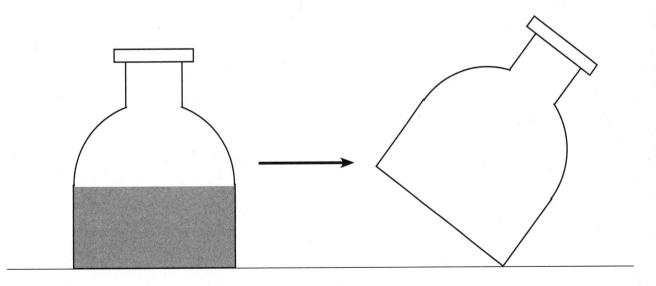

FOSS Next Generation
© The Regents of the University of California
Can be duplicated for classroom or workshop use.

Solids and Liquids Module
Investigation 2 I-Check
Page 3

INVESTIGATION 3 I-CHECK
SOLIDS AND LIQUIDS

1. Glass 1 has cornmeal in it. What happens when you pour cornmeal on the table?
   Draw and describe what the cornmeal looks like on the table.

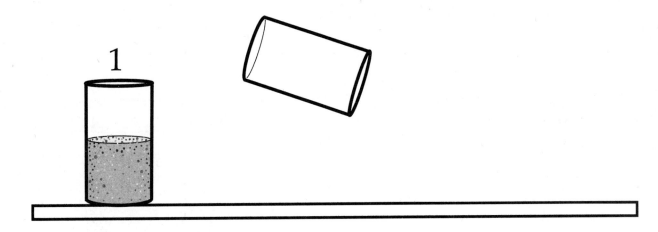

When you pour cornmeal, it _____ .

2. Glass 2 has water in it. What happens when you pour water on the table?
   Draw and describe what the water looks like on the table.

When you pour water, it _____ .

FOSS Next Generation
© The Regents of the University of California
Can be duplicated for classroom or workshop use.

Solids and Liquids Module
Investigation 3 I-Check
Page 1

INVESTIGATION 3 I-CHECK
SOLIDS AND LIQUIDS

3. Container 1 is filled with water. Container 2 is filled with gravel.
   If you drop one marble in each container, where would the marbles go?

   Draw one marble in each container.

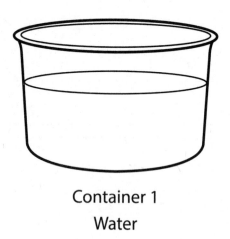

Container 1
Water

Container 2
Gravel

4. **Circle** all the beads that will go through the screen.
   Put an **X** on all the beads that will stay on top of the screen.

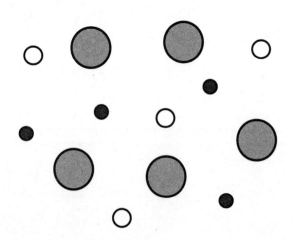

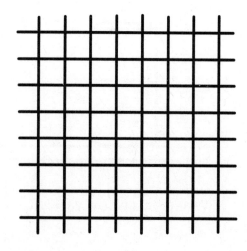

FOSS Next Generation
© The Regents of the University of California
Can be duplicated for classroom or workshop use.

Solids and Liquids Module
Investigation 3 I-Check
Page 2

1.   What happens when you put a spoon of peanut butter in water?

a.   Draw what you would see before shaking.

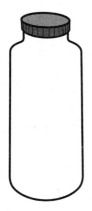

b.   Draw what you would see after shaking.

c.   Draw what you would see a day later.

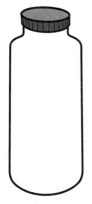

d.   Pour some of the liquid into a dish. Draw what you would see after evaporation.

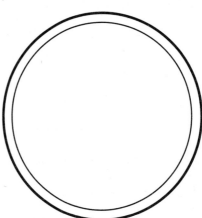

FOSS Next Generation
© The Regents of the University of California
Can be duplicated for classroom or workshop use.

Solids and Liquids Module
Investigation 4 I-Check
Page 1

INVESTIGATION 4 I-CHECK
SOLIDS AND LIQUIDS
· ·

2. This is a picture of ice cream on a stick, sitting in a cup.

    Circle a letter to label each object as a solid (**S**), liquid (**L**), or gas (**G**).

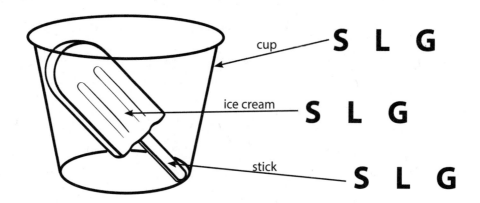

cup   **S L G**

ice cream   **S L G**

stick   **S L G**

Draw what happens to the ice cream and stick after sitting outside in the warm sunshine. Label the solids and liquids.

Describe what happens.

The ice cream _____ because _____

_____ .

The stick _____ because _____

_____ .

FOSS Next Generation
© The Regents of the University of California
Can be duplicated for classroom or workshop use.

Solids and Liquids Module
Investigation 4 I-Check
Page 2

INVESTIGATION 4 I-CHECK
SOLIDS AND LIQUIDS

3. You place the melted ice cream into a freezer. Draw a picture to show what it looks like after it freezes again.

Now it is frozen.

Is the ice cream hard or soft?_____

Describe the shape of the ice cream now._____

_____

FOSS Next Generation
© The Regents of the University of California
Can be duplicated for classroom or workshop use.

Solids and Liquids Module
Investigation 4 I-Check
Page 3

INVESTIGATION 4 I-CHECK
SOLIDS AND LIQUIDS

4. Write R in the box next to changes that are reversible.

   Write I in the box next to changes that are irreversible.

☐ Baking a cake.

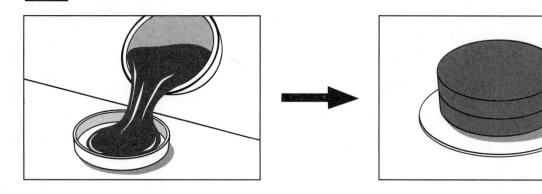

☐ Water freezing in the winter.

☐ Frying an egg.

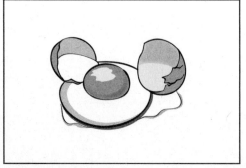

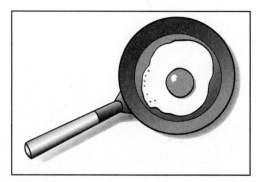

FOSS Next Generation
© The Regents of the University of California
Can be duplicated for classroom or workshop use.

Solids and Liquids Module
Investigation 4 I-Check
Page 4